Glencoe Science

LAB MANUAL

Forensics

Biology Online
glencoe.com

New York, New York Columbus, Ohio Chicago, Illinois

The McGraw·Hill Companies

Send all inquiries to:
Glencoe/McGraw-Hill
8787 Orion Place
Columbus, OH 43240-4027

ISBN-13: 978-0-07-874716-8
ISBN-10: 0-07-874716-3

Printed in the United States of America.

7 8 9 10 11 12 RHR 14 13 12

Table of Contents

To the Teacher iv

Correlation to Glencoe Biology Programs v

Safety and Disposal of Lab Materials vi

Forensics Materials Supply List viii

Suppliers ix

Lab 1 Where did they drown? 1

Lab 2 Can fingerprint analysis connect a suspect to a crime scene? 7

Lab 3 The Importance of Trace Evidence in Forensic Science 11

Lab 4 Can insect evidence establish time of death? 15

Lab 5 Forensic Odontology at Work 19

Lab 6 Crime Scene Investigation 23

Lab 7 When did she die? 25

Lab 8 A Sweet Season 29

Lab 9 Use Blood Types to Help Solve a Crime 33

Lab 10 The Missing Restaurant Owner 37

Teacher Guide and Answers 41

To the Teacher

Glencoe's Forensics Lab Manual features ten investigations that use forensics techniques to solve real-world problems. This series of investigative hands-on labs is easily integrated into your curriculum. Lab activities emphasize the use of scientific inquiry as a way of thinking and problem solving while relating scientific processes to technological and societal issues.

Students often benefit from a relevant frame of reference for learning abstract concepts. The goal of these labs is to involve students, usually working cooperatively, in extended, in-depth science experiences investigating DNA, collecting and analyzing data, or interpreting evidence found at a crime or accident scene.

Each lab begins with *The Problem*, which describes the discovery of a crime or accident. Information is presented in *Background* to guide students' understanding of the nature of science by collecting and analyzing data to solve a problem. In *Procedure*, students are given suggestions for completing the lab using steps that teach science process skills, such as observing and inferring. While participating in these labs, students will be confronted with topics such as inheritance and genetically related diseases, pathology, and blood types. The lab's final sections, *Conclude and Apply* and *Analyze and Conclude*, emphasize the importance of accurate recording and interpretation of data.

In the *Teacher Guide*, you will find the answer guide along with lab materials and supply lists, teaching strategies, expected outcomes, suggestions for time management, and tips for managing classroom activities.

Correlation to Glencoe Biology Programs

The activities in *Glencoe's Forensics Lab Manual* coordinate with the following chapters/units in these Glencoe biology programs. Use this chart to help plan the best way to use these activities with your class.

	Glencoe Biology	*BSCS Biology: A Molecular Approach*	*Biology: An Everyday Experience*	*Biology: Living Systems*
Lab 1: Where did they drown?	Chapter 7	Chapter 3	Chapter 2	Chapter 4
Lab 2: Can fingerprint analysis connect a suspect to a crime scene?	Chapter 32	Chapter 21	Chapters 13, 16	Chapter 5
Lab 3: The Importance of Trace Evidence in Forensic Science	Chapter 32		Chapter 13	
Lab 4: Can insect evidence establish time of death?	Chapter 26	Chapters 7, 18	Chapter 8	Chapter 17
Lab 5: Forensic Odontology at Work	Chapter 35	Chapter 2	Chapter 10	Chapter 20
Lab 6: Crime Scene Investigation	Chapter 1	Prologue	Chapter 1	Chapter 2
Lab 7: When did she die?	Chapters 32, 35	Chapters 2, 7	Chapter 10	Chapters 20, 26
Lab 8: A Sweet Season	Chapter 35	Chapter 9	Chapter 15	Chapter 24
Lab 9: Use Blood Types to Help Solve a Crime	Chapter 11	Chapter 13	Chapter 12	Chapter 21
Lab 10: The Missing Restaurant Owner	Chapters 11, 12, 13	Chapters 13, 15	Chapters 12, 28	Chapters 10, 21

Safety and Disposal of Lab Materials

Teaching science requires the use of certain supplies and safety equipment to maintain a safe classroom. The activities in ***Glencoe's Forensics Lab Manual*** minimize dangers in the laboratory. Even so, there are no guarantees against accidents. For additional help, refer to the booklet ***Glencoe Laboratory Management and Safety in the Science Classroom,*** which contains safety guidelines and masters to test students' lab and safety skills.

General Guidelines

- Post safety guidelines, fire escape routes, and a list of emergency procedures in the classroom. Make sure students understand these procedures. Remind them at the beginning of *every* lab session.
- Understand and make note of the safety symbols used in the activities.
- Have students fill out a safety contract. Students should pledge to follow the rules, to wear safety attire, and to conduct themselves in a responsible manner.
- Know where emergency equipment is stored and how to use it.
- Perform all activities before you allow students to do so.
- Supervise students at all times. Check assembly of all setups.
- Instruct students to follow directions carefully and to not take shortcuts or switch steps.
- Make sure that all students are wearing proper safety attire. Do not permit wearing contact lenses, even with safety glasses; splashing chemicals could infuse under a lens and cause eye damage.

Handling Electronic Equipment

- Instruct students on the safety guidelines provided by the manufacturer of your calculator(s) and probe(s).
- Check wiring for damage before each use. Do not use if frayed.
- Do not use the equipment where it could get wet.
- Do not allow students to eat or drink while using the equipment.
- Unplug the calculator when not in use.
- Caution students to use care when handling the equipment. Calculators and probes should not be shaken or dropped.
- Store the equipment properly when not in use.

Handling Chemicals

- Always wear safety goggles, gloves, and an apron when handling chemicals. Treat all chemicals as potentially dangerous.
- Never ingest chemicals. Use proper techniques to smell solutions.
- Use a fume hood when handling chemicals that are poisonous or corrosive or that give off a vapor.
- Know the location of an eyewash station. Flush the eyewash for five minutes once a week to remove harmful contaminants that may grow in the eyewash. Do not use a squeeze bottle as a substitute for an eyewash.
- Always add acids to water, never the reverse.
- Prepare solutions by adding the solid to a small amount of distilled water and then diluting with water to the volume listed. If you use a hydrate that is different from the one specified in a particular preparation, you will need to adjust the amount of hydrate to obtain the correct concentration.
- Consider purchasing premixed solutions from a scientific supply house to reduce the amount of chemicals on hand.
- Maintain appropriate MSDS (Materials Safety Data Sheets) in the laboratory.

Chemical Storage

- Use wood shelving, rather than metal, that is firmly attached to the wall.
- Equip shelves with a lip to prevent chemicals from being jarred off the shelf.

DISCLAIMER

Glencoe/McGraw-Hill makes no claims to the completeness of this discussion of laboratory safety and chemical storage. The information presented is not all-inclusive, nor does it address all of the hazards associated with the handling, storage, and disposal of chemicals, or with laboratory practices and management.

Forensics Materials Supply List

Labs	Everyday Materials	Lab Materials
Lab 1: Where did they drown?	tissues marker string (optional)	distilled water 25-mL graduated cylinder 250-mL graduated cylinder 250-mL beakers (7) balance that is sensitive to at least 0.1 g 2.5-cm x 30-cm pieces of water-soaked dialysis tubing (7) sucrose solutions (1%, 5%, 10%, 20%, 40%)
Lab 2: Can fingerprint analysis connect a suspect to a crime scene?	photocopies of suspects' fingerprints photocopy of fingerprint obtained from the office	magnifying lens or microscope
Lab 3: The Importance of Trace Evidence in Forensic Science		compound light microscope/magnifying lens glass slides and coverslips forceps dropper known fiber samples Fibers A and B from victim's clothing Fibers C and D from suspect's car known hair samples Hairs A and B from victim's clothing Hair C from suspect's head Hair D from victim's head
Lab 4: Can insect evidence establish time of death?	calculator ruler	
Lab 5: Forensic Odontology at Work	ruler	model of human teeth crime scene food item
Lab 6: Crime Scene Investigation	graph paper	
Lab 7 When did she die?	calculator graph paper ruler	your Biology textbook
Lab 8 A Sweet Season	tissues ruler graph paper watch with a second hand display or stopwatch	labeled test tubes (12) glucose test strips (12) copy of test strip color chart
Lab 9 Use Blood Types to Help Solve a Crime	bleach paper towels	ABO/Rh blood-typing test kit (with artificial or aseptic blood samples)
Lab 10 The Missing Restaurant Owner	paper pencil	your Biology textbook

Suppliers

American Science & Surplus
P.O. Box 1030
Skokie, IL 60076
1-847-647-0011
www.sciplus.com

Arbor Scientific
P.O. Box 2750
Ann Arbor, MI 48106-2750
(734) 477-9370
www.arborsci.com

Bio-Rad Laboratories
2000 Alfred Nobel Dr.
Life Science Group
Hercules, CA 94547
(800) 876-3425
www.biorad.com

Carolina Biological Supply Co.
2700 York Road
Burlington, NC 27215
(800) 334-5551
www.carolina.com

Chem Scientific, LLC
1250 Washington Street
Norwood, MA 02062
(888) 527-5827
www.chemscientific.com

Edmund Scientifics
60 Pearce Ave.
Tonawanda, NY 14150-6711
(800) 728-6999
www.scientificsonline.com

Fisher Science Education
4500 Turnberry
Hanover Park, IL 60133
(800) 955-1177
www.fisheredu.com

Flinn Scientific
P.O. Box 219
770 N. Raddant Rd.
Batavia, IL 60510
(800) 452-1261
www.flinnsci.com

Frey Scientific
P.O. Box 8101
100 Paragon Parkway
Mansfield, OH 44903
(800) 225-3739
www.freyscientific.com

Nasco Science
901 Janesville Avenue
P.O. Box 901
Fort Atkinson, WI 53538-0901
(800) 558-9595
www.enasco.com

Nebraska Scientific
3823 Leavenworth St.
Omaha, NE 68105-1180
(800) 228-7117
www.nebraskascientific.com

Pasco Scientific
10101 Foothills Blvd.
Roseville, CA 95747
(800) 772-8700
www.pasco.com

Sargent-Welch/VWR Scientific Products
P.O. Box 5229
Buffalo Grove, IL 60089-5229
(800) 727-4368
www.sargentwelch.com

Science Kit and Boreal Laboratories
777 East Park Dr.
P.O. Box 5003
Tonawanda, NY 14150
(800) 828-7777
www.sciencekit.com

VWR CanLab
2360 Argentina Rd.
Mississauga, Ontario
L5N5Z7
(800) 932-5000
www.vwrcanlab.com

Ward's Natural Science Establishment, Inc.
5100 W. Henrietta Road
P.O. Box 92912
Rochester, NY 14692-9012
(800) 962-2660
www.wardsci.com

Name Date Class

Where did they drown?

The Problem

The Coast Guard discovered two bodies, a man and a woman, in the salt water of the San Francisco Bay. Both victims apparently drowned; their lungs were filled with water, and a frothy mixture of water, air, and mucus was found in their mouths and airways. Your job as the coroner will be to determine where the victims drowned and whether the victims died of accidental drowning or were victims of murder. To help you in your determination, you have taken blood samples from both victims. You must interpret the findings from these blood samples to solve the mystery.

Background

Our bodies contain many compartments of liquid water, such as blood, tissues, and fluids between tissues. This water is composed of many substances, including salts, sugars, and proteins which have dissolved in the water. The concentration of any given substance is the amount of that substance per unit volume of water. Cells, such as those found in the walls of blood vessels and tissues, separate the various compartments of water. The membranes of these cells control which molecules can move between the compartments by allowing some molecules to pass through while limiting others. This is known as selective permeability.

Diffusion How do you know which way substances will move through a membrane? Generally, substances move from an area of high concentration to an area of low concentration. This movement is called diffusion. Diffusion occurs in solids, liquids, and gases. For example, if you cut an onion at the back of your classroom, people at the front of the room will eventually be able to smell it because molecules from the onion are transmitted (diffused) from an area of high concentration (the back of the room) to an area of low concentration (the front of the room). Diffusion continues until the concentration of molecules from the onion in the air is equal in all areas of the room.

All substances, including water, can diffuse. However, the diffusion of water across a selectively permeable membrane has a different name, *osmosis*. Suppose you have two solutions of sugar of different concentrations (high and low) in a clear box. A membrane that is permeable to water but not to sugar separates the two solutions. High concentration is on the left side, and low concentration is on the right side, as shown in Part A of **Figure 1**. The solution on the left has a higher sugar concentration relative to the one on the right and is said to be *hypertonic* to the one on the right. The solution on the right has a lower sugar concentration compared to the one on the left and is said to be *hypotonic* to the solution on the left.

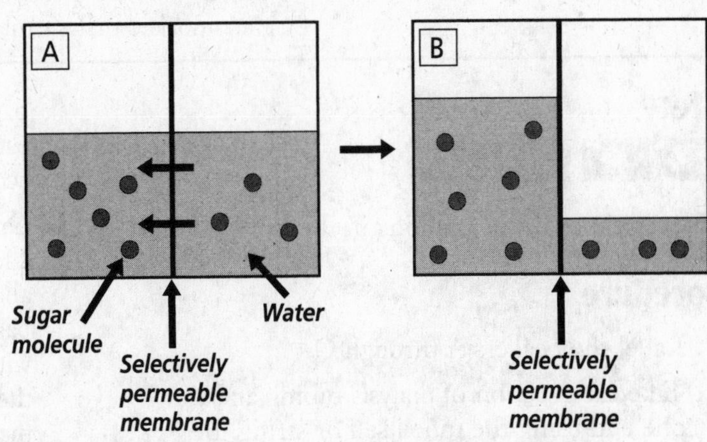

Figure 1

Where did they drown? *continued*

The more sugar that is dissolved in water, the less concentrated the water becomes; in other words, pure water is 100% water, and the concentration of water decreases as you add sugar. Therefore, the concentration of water on the left side is less than that on the right side. As a result, water will diffuse from the right to the left until the concentrations of water on both sides of the membrane are equal, as shown in Part B of **Figure 1**. At that time, the concentrations of sugar on both sides of the membrane will also be equal, or *isotonic*. Solutions in your body behave the same way.

Diffusion in the Lungs Your lungs form a compartment of air separated from a compartment of water (your blood) by cells that make up the air sacs called alveoli. When you breathe, gases diffuse from one compartment to another. Oxygen diffuses from the air into the blood, and carbon dioxide from the blood diffuses into the air. When a person drowns, the lungs fill with freshwater or salt water, depending on the type of water in which he or she drowned. The blood and lungs become two water-filled compartments (similar to **Figure 1**) in which water can move across the membranes separating the blood and the lungs. Salts in the compartments do not move across the membranes.

In this lab, you will simulate what happens in the human body when a person drowns. You will use sugar solutions to represent the solutions of water, salt, and other substances found in the lungs and blood. Solutions in beakers represent the blood; dialysis tubes, which are selectively permeable membranes, represent the alveoli of the lungs; and solutions in the dialysis tubes represent water in the lungs. You will first experiment with several beakers and dialysis tubes containing different concentrations of sugar representing hypertonic, hypotonic, and isotonic solutions. These will help you understand the movement of water that occurs with the differing solutions. Finally, two solution combinations will represent what happens when a person drowns in freshwater and in salt water.

Everyday Materials

- ❑ string (optional)
- ❑ tissues
- ❑ marker

Lab Materials

- ❑ sucrose solutions (1%, 5%, 10%, 20%, 40%)
- ❑ 250-mL beakers (7)
- ❑ 2.5 cm × 30 cm pieces of water-soaked dialysis tubing (7)
- ❑ distilled water
- ❑ 250-mL graduated cylinder
- ❑ 25-mL graduated cylinder
- ❑ balance that is sensitive to at least 0.1 g

Safety

- Never eat or drink anything in the lab.

Procedure

1. Label the beakers A through G.
2. Take each section of dialysis tubing and tie one end using the tube itself or string. Be careful not to tear the bag.
3. Fill each dialysis tube with 25 mL of sucrose solution, according to the table on the next page. The tubes should be about $\frac{1}{3}$ full. Fill each beaker with 150 mL of sucrose solution according to the table.
4. Once you fill a dialysis bag, squeeze the air out and tie the remaining end a few centimeters above the top of the liquid without tearing the bag. Rinse the bag with distilled water, blot it dry with a tissue, and weigh it on the balance. Record the mass in the table on the next page (initial bag mass) and place the bag in the appropriate beaker. Repeat this procedure for each bag.
5. Allow each bag to stay in the beaker for 30 minutes.

Name Date Class

Lab 1

Where did they drown? *continued*

6. After 30 minutes, remove each bag, rinse with distilled water, blot dry, and determine its mass. Record the mass in the table (final bag mass). Measure the amount of liquid that remains in the beaker after the bag is removed. Discard the bags and empty the beakers.

7. Calculate the change in each bag's mass (final mass – initial mass) and the percent change $\left(\frac{\text{mass change}}{\text{initial mass}} \times 100\right)$. Record the values in the table below and use the data to answer the questions.

Table 1

Beaker	Bag Sol	Beaker Sol	Initial Bag Mass	Final Bag Mass	Mass Change	%Change
A	10%	1%				
B	10%	5%				
C	10%	10%				
D	10%	20%				
E	10%	40%				
F	1%	10%				
G	40%	10%				

Conclude and Apply

1. What happened to the mass of Bags A and B during the experiment?

2. Were the concentrations of the solutions in Beakers A and B more than or less than the concentrations of the solutions inside the bags? Would you classify the solutions in the beakers as hypertonic, hypotonic, or isotonic relative to the solution inside the bag? (Refer to the *Background* section for more information.)

3. Explain the changes observed in Bags A and B in terms of the concentrations of solutions inside and outside the bags and the movement of water.

4. What happened to the mass of Bag C?

Where did they drown? *continued*

5. How did the solution in Beaker C compare to the solution inside the bag? Would you classify it as hypertonic, hypotonic, or isotonic relative to the solution inside the bag?

6. Explain any changes observed in Bag C in terms of the concentrations of solutions inside and outside the bag and the movement of water.

7. What happened to the masses of Bags D and E during the experiment?

8. Were the concentrations of the solutions in Beakers D and E more than or less than the concentrations of the solutions inside the bags? Would you classify the solutions in the beakers as hypertonic, hypotonic, or isotonic relative to the solution inside the bag? (Refer to the *Background* section for more information.)

Lab 1 Where did they drown? *continued*

9. Explain the changes observed in Bags D and E in terms of the concentrations of solutions inside and outside the bags and the movement of water.

10. Beaker F represents a person who drowned in freshwater. The bag represents the lungs, and the solution in the beaker represents the blood. The 1% sucrose inside the bag approximates the total salt concentration in freshwater, while the 10% sucrose in the beaker approximates the total salt concentration in the blood. What happened to the mass of the bag? Did water move out of the bag or into the bag? What happened to the concentration of sucrose in the beaker? Explain.

11. Beaker G represents a person who drowned in salt water. The 40% sucrose inside the bag approximates the total salt concentration in salt water, while the 10% sucrose in the beaker approximates the total salt concentration in the blood. What happened to the mass of the bag? Did water move out of the bag or into the bag? What happened to the concentration of sucrose in the beaker? Explain.

Analyze and Conclude

12. The following table contains the concentrations (in millimoles per liter) of various substances in the blood of the two drowning victims. Just as the term *dozen* refers to a specific number of things (12), the term *mole* refers to a specific number of particles (6.02×10^{23}). A millimole is 1/1000th of a mole. When concentration is given in millimoles (or moles) per liter, higher numbers indicate more particles dissolved in the water—in the table below, higher concentrations of sodium, potassium, or chloride.

Table 2

Concentration (mmole/L)			
Substance	**Man**	**Woman**	**Normal Values**
Sodium	200	100	145
Potassium	10	2	5
Chloride	125	75	100

Where do you think each victim drowned? Explain your answer.

13. Should you look for murderers or did the victims drown accidentally? Explain your answer.

Name Date Class

Lab 2 Can fingerprint analysis connect a suspect to a crime scene?

The Problem

A computer hard drive has been taken from a tenth-floor office in a government building. Files on the drive include personal information about specific government employees. Federal Bureau of Investigation agents are concerned the data might be used by imposters to access secure sites or information. The investigation is focused on two men. The first is employed by a company that frequently caters early breakfast meetings in the conference rooms, which are located on the second floor. The second man works for a pest control company that services the building. Both suspects claim that they have never been above the second floor of the building.

Multiple fingerprints have been obtained from the office. Most of them match those of government workers, whose fingerprints were recorded when they were hired. However, one fingerprint found on a countertop in the office does not match any employee working in the building. The Integrated Automated Fingerprint Identification System, the national fingerprint and criminal history system maintained by the FBI, also shows no match. If the fingerprints of either suspect match the unidentified fingerprint found in the office, a suspect can be placed at the crime scene. In this lab, you will analyze and compare fingerprints to determine if either of the suspects' fingerprints match the unidentified impression.

Background

Friction Ridges and Fingerprints Friction ridges are raised ridges of skin on human fingers, palms, and soles of the feet. This hairless skin provides a gripping surface, much like tire treads. Because friction ridges are lined with small sweat pores, a layer of perspiration forms along the tops of the ridges. This sweat can mix with body oils and dirt, producing impressions when fingertips contact surfaces. Fingerprints are often visible on metal, glass, or plastic. When invisible, fingerprints can be detected and developed using special lighting, X rays, or various chemical processes. Impressions are then photographed to create a visible record.

Friction Ridge Characteristics Friction ridge characteristics can be grouped. Refer to **Figure 1** as you read each description.

- *ridge ending* – a ridge that ends suddenly
- *bifurcation* – a ridge that divides into two ridges
- *lake* – a ridge that divides, comes together again close to the bifurcation, and continues on as a single ridge
- *short ridge* – a ridge that travels a small distance
- *dot* – a short ridge with approximately equal width and length
- *spur* – a bifurcation with a short ridge branching off a longer ridge
- *crossover* – a ridge that runs between two parallel ridges

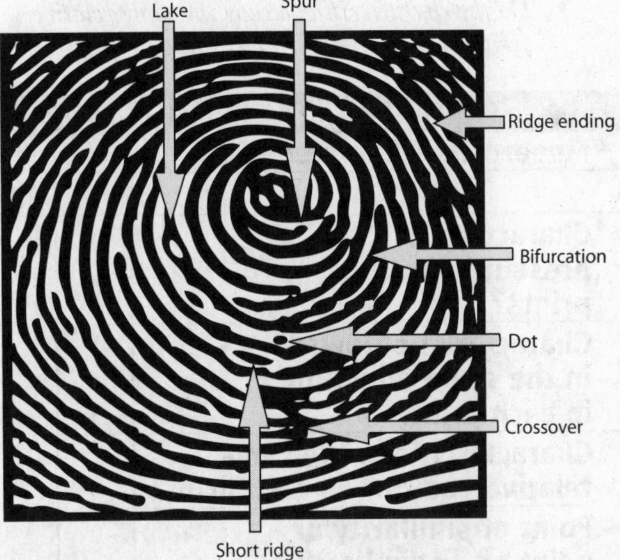

Figure 1

Lab 2

Can fingerprint analysis connect a suspect to a crime scene?

continued

Using Fingerprints for Identification Two principles make it possible to use fingerprints to identify individuals.

1. ***Friction ridge patterns do not change over time.*** Friction ridge patterns develop between the third and fourth months of pregnancy. While patterns can be altered by an accident or skin disease, aging has no effect on friction ridge patterns.
2. ***No two people have the same pattern of friction ridges.*** There is enough variability in friction ridge characteristics to ensure that no two people have identical fingerprints. Humans have different ridge patterns on each finger, and identical twins can be differentiated by their fingerprints.

Materials

- ❑ photocopies of suspects' fingerprints
- ❑ photocopy of fingerprint obtained from the office

Procedure

1. Using **Figure 1** as a guide, label 15 characteristics of Suspect A's fingerprint on the photocopies provided. Assign a number to each characteristic labeled.
2. Repeat step 1 with Suspect B's fingerprint and the unidentified fingerprint.
3. Compare Suspect A's fingerprint to the unidentified fingerprint. Think about these questions as you look at the two impressions.
   - *Are the same characteristics present in both fingerprints?*
   - *Do the characteristics of both fingerprints flow in the same direction?*
   - *Do the characteristics occupy the same relative positions to each other in both fingerprints?*
4. Focus on a single characteristic of Suspect A's fingerprint. Compare it to the unidentified fingerprint by answering the questions in the data chart. If the answer to all three questions is "yes," the characteristic is called a point of similarity. If the answer to any of the questions is "no," the characteristic is called a point of dissimilarity. Note: When a single unexplainable point of dissimilarity is found, it is assumed there is no match between the fingerprints.
5. Examine characteristics until ten points of similarity are established, or a single point of dissimilarity is found.
6. Repeat step 4 using Suspect B's fingerprint.

Fingerprint Comparison: Suspect A and Unidentified Fingerprint

Fingerprint Characteristics										
	1	2	3	4	5	6	7	8	9	10
Characteristic present in both prints?										
Characteristic flows in the same direction in each print?										
Characteristic in the same relative position in each print?										
Point of similarity or point of dissimilarity?										

Lab 2

Can fingerprint analysis connect a suspect to a crime scene?

continued

Fingerprint Comparison: Suspect B and Unidentified Fingerprint										
Fingerprint Characteristics										
	1	**2**	**3**	**4**	**5**	**6**	**7**	**8**	**9**	**10**
Characteristic present in both prints?										
Characteristic flows in the same direction in each print?										
Characteristic in the same relative position in each print?										
Point of similarity or point of dissimilarity?										

Conclude and Apply

1. Compare the number of points of similarity and points of dissimilarity identified in the two fingerprint comparisons you conducted.

2. Based on the data, decide among the following choices: there is a match between two fingerprints, there is no match between two fingerprints, or the comparison is inconclusive. Justify your decision.

3. Were either of the suspects lying about having been at the crime scene? On a scale of 1–5 (1 being lowest, 5 being highest), rank your level of confidence in your answer, and explain why you feel this way.

Name Date Class

Lab 2

Can fingerprint analysis connect a suspect to a crime scene? *continued*

Analyze and Conclude

4. Fingerprint analyses do not rely on numerical measurements of things like the angle formed by a bifurcation, or the precise distance between two given characteristics. Why do fingerprint examiners use a comparison approach rather than a quantifiable approach when studying and comparing impressions?

5. There is currently no international standard for the number of points of similarity required to determine a fingerprint match. Some countries require as many as 20; others require from 8 to 12. In your opinion, are 10 points of similarity adequate to determine a fingerprint match? Explain your answer.

Name Date Class

Lab 3 The Importance of Trace Evidence in Forensic Science

The Problem

At 2 A.M. on a Wednesday morning, university police received a call from a student worried about his roommate. He reported that the young man left his dormitory room to go running at 8 P.M. Tuesday evening and had not returned. The student told police that his roommate was typically back at the dorm within one to two hours after leaving for a run. In the past several months, three university students had been robbed at knifepoint while walking on the campus after dark. While a suspect had been identified by police, the assailant had not been arrested, and many students were concerned.

Within 24 hours, search dogs assisting an investigation team alerted to the young man's scent. His body was discovered in a lightly wooded area off a secondary road roughly two miles from his dormitory. The victim, identified by his roommate, was wearing the running clothes and shoes he was last seen alive in two days before. Based on evidence found at the scene, the man suspected of the local armed robberies was brought in for questioning. No witnesses were found, and no weapons were uncovered at the scene. Police confiscated the suspect's car for further investigation.

As a pathologist assigned to the investigation, you determine the cause of death as asphyxiation resulting from strangulation. You recover a number of fiber samples from the victim's clothing, and find numerous hair strands between the fingers of his right hand and on his sweatshirt. Your job is to determine if properties of the trace evidence found on the victim are consistent with samples taken from the suspect and his car.

Background

When a person is physically involved in a crime, some trace of his or her presence is generally left behind. This concept, called *Locard's Principle of Exchange*, forms the primary basis for forensic investigations. The term *trace evidence* is used to describe objects found in small amounts at a crime scene that may hold clues about what took place. Trace evidence can place a suspect at a crime scene, or connect a victim to a suspect in some way. While there are many types of trace evidence, including paint chips, gunshot residue particles, dirt, pollen, and glass fragments, investigations often focus on textile fibers and hair.

Fiber Evidence Fibers make up materials like clothing, carpeting, furniture, bedding, and wigs. Natural fibers include cotton, linen, and wool. Polyester, nylon, and rayon are artificial fibers. Materials shed fibers, and when there is contact between two people or a person and a fabric-covered object, fibers can be transferred. Fibers are gathered at a crime scene using tweezers, tape, or a specially adapted vacuum cleaner. In most cases, there are a limited number of fibers available for examination; sometimes there is only one. In general, the more fibers present, the greater the likelihood that contact occurred. Whether or not fibers are ultimately found on the victim or the suspect is affected by various factors, including the specific fabrics involved and the type of contact that occurs.

Fiber Analysis Fiber analysts compare the color and diameter of fibers to determine a possible match. They analyze fiber dye content and chemical composition, and look for characteristics like unusual shape and striations or pits on the fiber surface. Fiber analysis alone cannot form the basis for a case against a suspect. Unlike fingerprints or DNA, fibers are not unique. A gray wool fiber that comes from a sweater will have similar characteristics to a gray wool fiber that comes from a blanket. However, while it is impossible to prove that a fiber came from a specific piece of clothing or other specific source, the presence of similar fibers can support other evidence or even prompt a confession.

Hair Evidence Like fibers, hair evidence has limitations. While a hair from a crime scene may have properties that make it consistent with a sample from a suspect, hair is rarely used to make a definitive identification. Only hair shafts attached to a follicle are relevant for DNA testing. Despite limitations, hair characteristics can identify the source as human or some other animal, establish the source's race, determine if the hair was dyed, cut in a certain way, or pulled out, and identify the body location from which the hair came.

Examples of Hair Characteristics Study **Figure 1** as you read each description.

Hair A: Human head hair, Caucasian origin. General characteristics: fine to medium in coarseness; straight or wavy; shafts are round to oval in cross section; color pigments are fine to medium-sized and evenly distributed through the shaft.

Hair B: Human head hair, Afro-Caribbean origin. General characteristics: curly or kinky; flattened cross section; pigment particles are large and grouped in dense clumps of different sizes and shapes; may be opaque.

Hair C: Human head hair, Asian origin. General characteristics: coarse; straight and circular in cross section; compared to hair of other racial groups, the cuticle, or outer layer, is thicker and the diameter is wider; medulla is continuous and wide, large pigment particles grouped in patchy areas; reddish appearance.

Hair D: Cat hair. General characteristics: fibrous roots; pigment particles do not run down to the root; the medulla, or inner layer of cells, is thicker than that of dog hair relative to the overall width of the hair.

Hair E: Dog hair. General characteristics: spade-like roots; pigmentation runs through the shaft to the root; medulla is thinner than that of cat hair relative to the overall width of the hair.

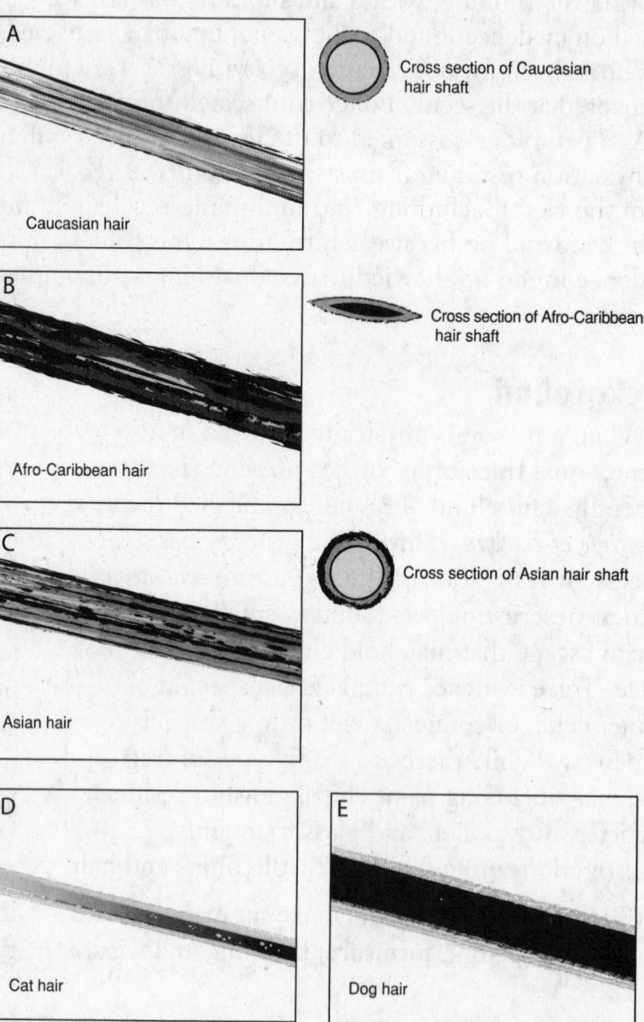

Figure 1

Lab 3 The Importance of Trace Evidence in Forensic Science *continued*

Materials

- ❑ compound light microscope/magnifying lens
- ❑ glass slides and cover slips
- ❑ forceps
- ❑ dropper
- ❑ known fiber samples
- ❑ Fibers A and B from victim's clothing
- ❑ Fibers C and D from suspect's car
- ❑ known hair samples
- ❑ Hairs A and B from victim's clothing
- ❑ Hair C from suspect's head
- ❑ Hair D from victim's head

Safety

- Always wear gloves, goggles, and apron.
- Handle forceps and glass slides carefully. Alert your teacher to broken glass, and dispose of in designated location.
- Keep you hands away from your eyes and face in science lab.
- Wash hands thoroughly after handling samples.
- Follow your teacher's instructions for disposal of lab materials.

Procedure

Part A: Investigating Known Fiber and Hair Samples

1. Create a data table with the headings shown below. Make the table wide enough to accommodate your observations.

Trace Evidence Data		
Examination of Fiber and Hair Samples Under Various Microscope Powers		
Source of Fiber/Source of Hair Shaft	**Sketch/Notes**	**Sketch/Notes**

2. Make a wet mount slide of each known fiber sample provided.
3. Use the microscope to examine each fiber under different magnifications. Make a sketch. Note features like color, pits, striations, amount of twist, fineness/coarseness, shape, and relative diameter.
4. Make a wet mount slide of each hair sample provided.
5. Use the microscope to examine each hair sample. Make a sketch. Note characteristics of the cuticle, cortex, and/or medulla. Compare samples to the information in **Figure 1.**

Part B: Comparison of Fiber and Hair Samples

1. Use the microscope to examine the prepared slides of Fiber A and Fiber B found on the victim's clothing. Make a sketch. Note fiber features, and identify the fiber type if possible. Note similarities and differences between the two fibers.
2. Use the microscope to examine Fiber C taken from a floor mat of the suspect's car, and Fiber D taken from carpet in the trunk of the suspect's car. Sketch both fibers. Your notes should include similarities and differences between these two fibers and those found on the victim's clothing.
3. Use the microscope to examine Hair A found between the victim's fingers and Hair B found on the victim's sweatshirt. Sketch both hairs, and note characteristics of each hair layer.
4. Use the microscope to examine Hair C taken from the suspect's head and Hair D taken from the victim's head. Sketch both hairs. Your notes should include similarities and differences between these two hairs and the hairs found on the victim.

Name Date Class

Lab 3

The Importance of Trace Evidence in Forensic Science *continued*

Conclude and Apply

1. Do either of the fibers taken from the suspect's car (Fiber C and Fiber D) share characteristics with fibers found on the victim's clothing (Fiber A and Fiber B)? Describe similarities between these fibers.

2. Based on fiber evidence alone, if the victim was in the suspect's car at some point during the night he went running, where in the car might he have been?

3. Is there any consistency between the hair samples you examined? Explain.

4. Based on hair evidence alone, is it possible that there was contact between the victim and the suspect on the night of the murder? Explain.

Analyze and Conclude

5. Does the presence of trace evidence on the victim's clothes and in his fingers prove that he was with the suspect or in the suspect's car on the night he was murdered? Explain.

6. Based on the your review of trace evidence, list of a series of events that *might* have taken place on the night of the murder.

7. Fiber and hair evidence might be used in this case to support other evidence. Describe other things investigators should uncover to establish a case against the suspect.

8. What sources of error could occur while obtaining the evidence?

Lab 4 Can insect evidence establish time of death?

The Problem

During the morning commute on October 9, a driver reported seeing a body in a wooded area beside a major road in a large city. The deceased was an adult female, approximately 55 kg in mass and 160 cm in height (120 pounds and 5'3"). On the day the body was discovered, investigators matched the victim's description to a current missing person report, and the deceased was identified as a 21-year-old woman who lived with her parents in an apartment complex close to the wooded area. The victim was last seen alive seven days prior to the discovery of the body in the apartment of the prime suspect, an acquaintance with a history of violent criminal behavior. The medical examiner, who was called to the scene, noted these conditions at the site before the body was removed for autopsy:

- rigor mortis absent
- body cold, decomposition in initial stages
- multiple stab wounds present in chest area
- several large maggots, roughly 15 millimeters in length, observed migrating away from the corpse; maggots captured for further investigation

Additional evidence pointed to the suspect. Hair from the victim's head shared characteristics with hair found on a chair in the suspect's apartment, blood and hair samples taken from the suspect's car showed a possible match to the victim, and carpet fibers removed from the victim's clothing matched fibers from the suspect's car. However, to build a case and establish a sequence of events surrounding the death, investigators need to determine time of death as accurately as possible.

As a forensic entomologist, you have been asked to apply your knowledge of insects and other forensic evidence to estimate when the victim died. You identify the maggots observed in and around the body as *Lucilia sericata*, a species of blow fly. While the maggots captured at the scene had since died, you determine the stage of development as third instar—the larva stage after the second molting—based on the length of the larvae, the size of their mouth parts, and other physical features. Because temperature affects the rate of blow fly development, you secure climatological data for the dates surrounding the murder and discovery of the body.

Temperature Data: October 2–10

Date	Minimum Temperature (°C)	Maximum Temperature (°C)
10/2	15.0	26.5
10/3	13.0	26.0
10/4	11.0	26.0
10/5	7.5	23.5
10/6	7.0	23.5
10/7	6.5	22.0
10/8	9.5	22.0
10/9	9.0	20.5

Lab 4 Can insect evidence establish time of death? *continued*

Background

A key component in any forensic examination is establishing time of death. An examiner is trained to interpret body changes, translating them into a time line of postmortem events. For example, body temperature decreases at a somewhat predictable rate after death. The rate of decrease and temperature of the corpse can help estimate time of death. While body temperature changes are affected by factors like body fat, air temperature, and clothing, other changes occur independently. For example, relaxed muscles begin to stiffen within one to two hours after death, producing a condition called rigor mortis. Muscles remain stiff up to 12 hours after death, then begin to relax again. Between 24 and 48 after death, muscles are again completely relaxed. Body changes are particularly useful within one to two days after death.

Forensic Entomology How can time of death be established if a body is found more than two or three days after death occurred? At this point, insects can provide vital information. Within minutes after death, certain insects are attracted to a corpse, especially if blood or other body fluids are present. The corpse supports an evolving ecosystem, as other insects arrive and begin to feed, grow, and lay eggs. A forensic entomologist can be called on to interpret this evidence.

Forensic entomology is based on several key principles.

1. **Forensically important insects proceed through predictable developmental stages.**
Blow flies are typically one of the first insects to arrive on a corpse. The blow fly life cycle is shown in **Figure 1.** The female lays eggs in body cavities and wounds. The first instar stage occurs when an egg hatches into a small larva. The larva feeds on dead tissue and grows quickly. When the larva grows to a certain size, it discards the exoskeleton and grows a larger one, a process called molting. Now at the second instar stage, the larva continues to feed and grow. The blow fly larva molts a third time, still feeding and growing. At this point, the fully developed third instar larva wanders away from the corpse to find a suitable site to form the puparium, in which final development occurs. When the adult blow fly emerges, one end of the puparium appears cut off, revealing the hollow interior.
2. **Forensically important insects lay eggs on a corpse relatively quickly.**
Under favorable climate conditions, blow flies lay eggs within the first hours of body exposure. This fact allows entomologists to establish time of death. If the age of blow fly larvae on a corpse can be determined, the entomologist can estimate when death occurred.
3. **Insect development depends on temperature.**
While the time required for blow flies to complete each developmental stage is known, scientists also know that development proceeds fastest in warm temperatures. For a body discovered in a temperature-controlled environment, it is easier to determine the time between stages of development. For a body left outside, however, temperature fluctuation is a factor the forensic entomologist must consider.

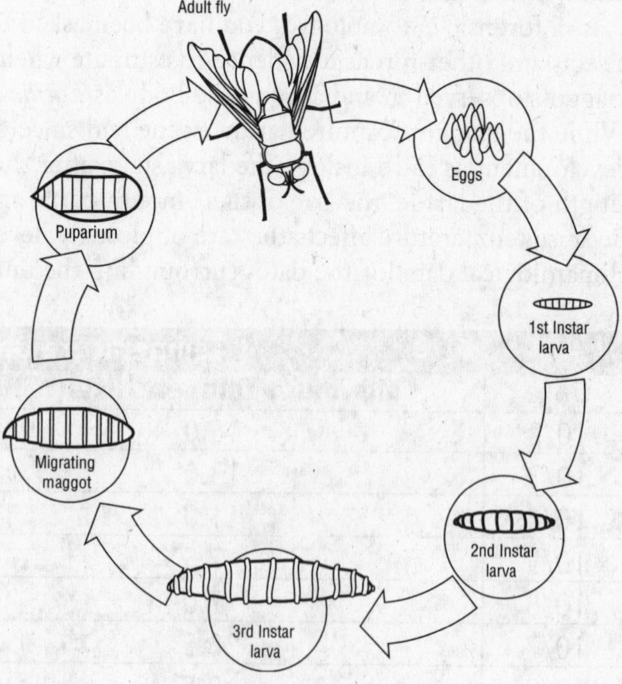

Figure 1

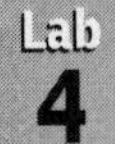

Lab 4 Can insect evidence establish time of death? *continued*

Materials

- ❑ calculator
- ❑ the instructions for this activity
- ❑ ruler

Procedure

1. Create a time line large enough to accommodate notes. Study the Problem section of this lab, and add data to the time line.

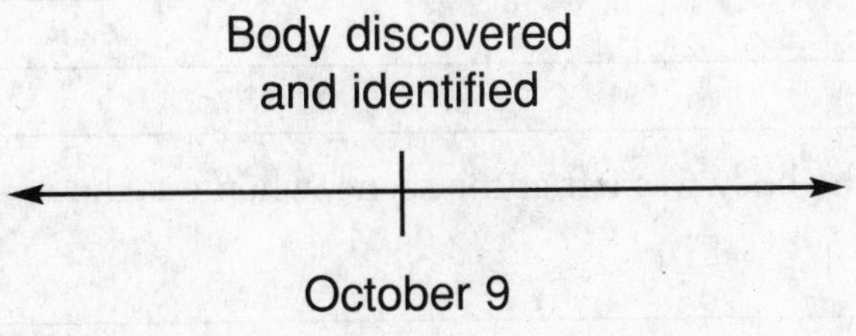

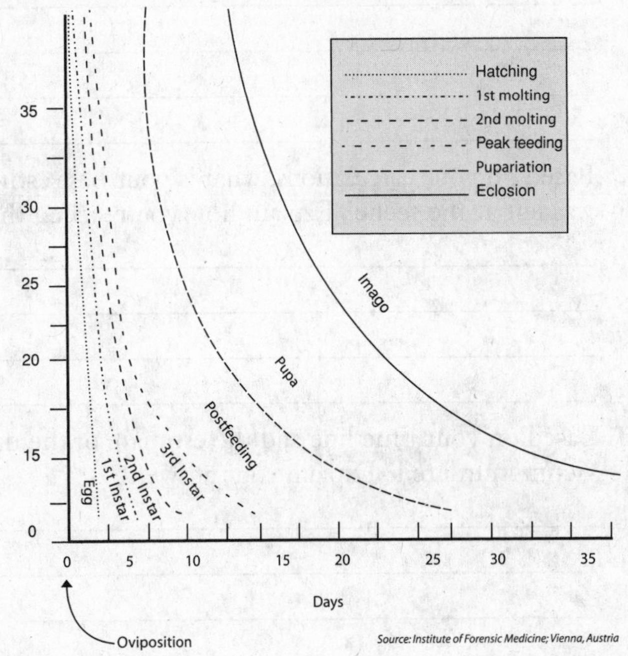

Figure 2

2. Based on the medical examiner's notes, narrow the time of death between October 9 and the last date the victim was seen alive. Note these dates on the time line.
3. Calculate the average temperature the body might have been exposed to during the dates on the time line. Calculate the average daily temperature for each date, then find the average temperature for the time period. Record these numbers on or beside the time line.
4. Use the average temperature for the period, the developmental stage of the larvae, and **Figure 2** to further narrow the range of time of death. Note this range on the time line.
5. Finally, use information about the length of the larvae, the average temperature, your knowledge of the larval developmental stage, and **Figure 3** to estimate when the victim's body was placed at the scene. Note the date on your time line.

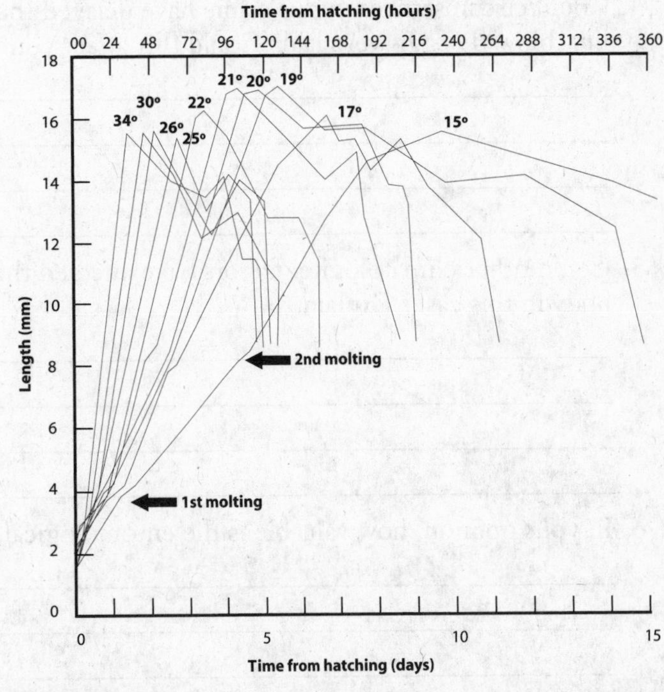

Figure 3

Lab 4

Can insect evidence establish time of death? *continued*

Conclude and Apply

1. Explain how knowing the developmental stage of the oldest blow fly larvae helped narrow the range of time of death in step 4 of the procedure.

2. Based on your calculations, what is your best estimate of the approximate date that the victim's body was left at the scene? Explain how you reached this conclusion.

3. Based on your time line and the estimate of the date the body was left at the scene, when was the victim murdered? Explain your answer.

Analyze and Conclude

4. Could circumstances in this crime have delayed the time between the victim's death and when the first blow fly eggs were laid? Could this affect your estimate of the time of death? Explain.

5. Could other climatological factors have affected the growth and development of larvae found on the body in this case? Explain.

6. In your opinion, how valuable is the entomological evidence in this case? Justify your answer.

Lab 5

Forensic Odontology at Work

The Problem

At 9:10 A.M. on December 6, police responded to a call from the owner of a delicatessen. The manager reported that cash and electronic equipment had been stolen from the shop. The crime occurred sometime between 7 P.M. on December 5 after the owner locked the shop for the evening and 7 A.M. the following morning. Investigators found one unusual piece of evidence at the scene: an unwrapped hunk of cheese was discovered in a refrigerated case with a large bite removed from it. A clear impression of teeth marks was preserved in the cheese.

Police had identified a suspect in several robberies that had occurred recently in the neighborhood of the delicatessen. Until this point, however, no evidence at any of the crime scenes had been found to link the suspect to the crimes. Investigators hope an analysis of the bite mark in the cheese might provide a way to link the suspect to this particular robbery, and perhaps to the others as well.

Background

Forensic odontology is an established branch of forensic science in which the principles of dental science are applied to legal matters. Forensic odontologists frequently assist investigators in identifying human remains, particularly in mass disaster situations like the New York City World Trade Center disaster in 2001. While their work in identifying unknown victims is perhaps most well known, forensic odontologists also use their expertise to analyze bite mark evidence on victims or inanimate objects present at crime scenes.

The theory underlying forensic odontology is that no two mouths are alike; an individual's dentition —the type, number, and arrangement of teeth—is believed to be unique. This makes a bite mark a valuable piece of evidence. A forensic odontologist can use teeth impressions left in foods like apples, cheese, chocolate, and even chewing gum to link a suspect to a victim or crime scene. When saliva is present in the impression, the potential for DNA analysis exists. Even when this is not possible, a dental impression alone can provide crucial information about the person who left it behind.

Value of Bite Marks in Food Teeth impressions in food are forensically important for several reasons.

1. **A bite mark left in food is three-dimensional.** A three-dimensional image provides information about multiple teeth surfaces, increasing the data available for analysis and comparison.
2. **Food evidence can be preserved.** Preserving agents like glycerol and formaldehyde make it possible to retain a dental impression for extended periods.
3. **There are up to 32 teeth in an adult human mouth.** A food impression rarely includes all teeth. However, the more teeth available for comparison between a suspect's mouth and an impression, the greater the level of confidence in the analysis.

Lab 5

Forensic Odontology at Work *continued*

Teeth in the Human Mouth Refer to **Figure 1** and **Figure 2** as you read each definition.

- *incisors* – Teeth 7–10 and 23–26. Generally chisel-shaped; function in nipping—the mouth action taken when biting into an apple.
- *canines* – Teeth 6, 11, 22, 27. Usually long with a pointed cusp; function in piercing and stabbing food.
- *premolars* – Teeth 4, 5, 12, 13. Have two cuspals, or points, and can be called bicuspids.
- *molars* – Teeth 1–3, 14–16, 17–19, 30–32. Generally have the greatest surface area; function in crushing.

Matching a Suspect's Dentition to Bite Mark Evidence A forensic odontologist follows a general procedure to determine the possibility of a match between a dental impression and a suspect's dentition.

1. Make a record of the suspect's dentition. Characteristics including the distance between canines, the shape of the mouth arch, tooth alignment, thickness, width and spacing, missing teeth, and any other unique features are recorded using written records and photography.
2. Create a permanent impression. The suspect makes a dental impression in a soft, silicon-based material. A permanent plaster cast of teeth and gums is made from this impression.
3. Compare the dental impression in the food item to the cast. In comparing the two impressions, the forensic odontologist looks for similar characteristics in teeth shape, size, and position, as well as any unique dental features that are present.

Figure 1

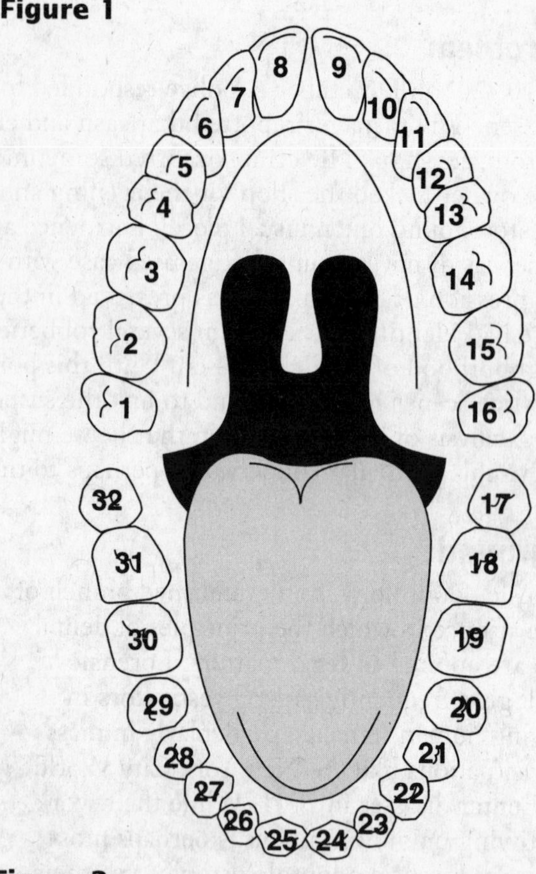

Figure 2

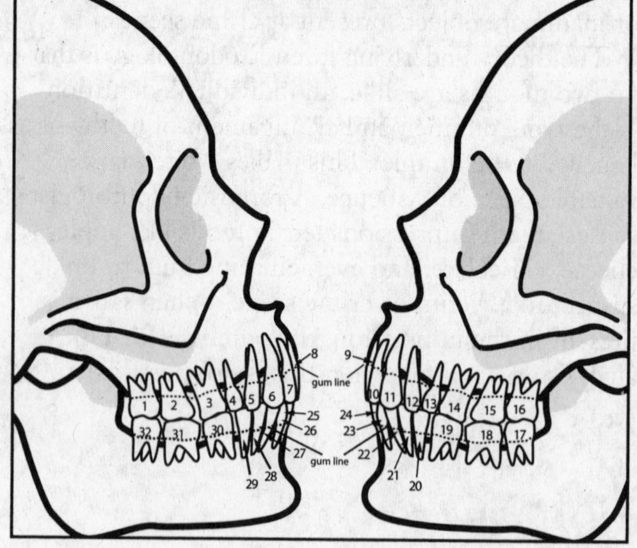

Name Date Class

Materials

- ❑ model of human teeth
- ❑ crime scene food item
- ❑ ruler

Safety

- Never taste anything in the lab.
- Keep your hands away from your eyes and face in the science lab.
- Wear gloves when handling the food item and dental impressions in this lab.
- Wash your hands thoroughly after each lab activity.

Procedure

1. Study the human teeth model. Number a list from 1–32, then use **Figure 1** and **Figure 2** to identify and write the name of each tooth in the model. Describe characteristics of each tooth on the list. Note similarities and differences among tooth types.
2. Compare both sections of the suspect's polystyrene dental impression with the human teeth model. Identify the type and location of each tooth represented by the impression.
3. Examine the suspect's top impression. Record the number of teeth in the impression. Record characteristics including spaces between teeth, rotated teeth or teeth out of alignment, the distances between specific teeth, and any other unusual features you notice.
4. Repeat step 3 with the suspect's bottom impression.
5. Next, study the impression in the food item. Note similarities and differences between the food item impression and the polystyrene impression.
6. Based on your observations, choose from the following descriptions:

Positive Identification
The suspect's dental impression matches the impression in the food item.

Possible Identification
While consistencies exist between impressions, there is not enough evidence to establish a match.

Insufficient Evidence
There is not enough information to reach a conclusion.

Exclusion
The suspect's dental impression does not match the impression in the food item.

Name Date Class

Conclude and Apply

1. Were you able to establish a match between the suspect's dental impression and the impression in the food item? Explain.

2. What characteristics of the suspect's dentition did you focus on when attempting to establish a match? Were certain teeth or some specific teeth characteristics more helpful than others? Explain.

Analyze and Conclude

3. How confident do you feel about your comparison of the two dental impressions? Explain.

4. Imagine you are the defense attorney for the suspect. What arguments could you use to damage the credibility of the evidence presented by the forensic odontologist regarding the dental impression comparison?

5. In most cases, a dental impression found in a food item at a crime scene does not show a full complement of teeth. What other types of evidence might a forensic scientist look for to provide additional information about the person who left the impression?

Name Date Class

Lab 6 Crime Scene Investigation

The Problem

On May 9, Colorado State Police are contacted by a woman living in Texas whose brother lives in a remote area north of Denver. Though she speaks with her brother by phone about once a month, she has not been able to reach him for a week. She is concerned; the phone conversations occur regularly, and she and her brother have not spoken for roughly five weeks. Officers sent to investigate the brother's home discover two bodies at the scene.

The body of a man is discovered on the right side of the back yard, about halfway between the house and a car parked in the driveway to the right rear of the house. This body carries no wallet and no identifying records. Another male victim is found on the kitchen floor. The driver's license in his wallet identifies him as the woman's brother and owner of the home. The kitchen is located in the right rear of the house. Two steps lead from the kitchen to the back yard, and one window in the kitchen is unscreened and open. An interior doorway leads from the kitchen to the den at the right front of the home.

The ground and floor around both bodies is stained with dried blood, and footprints are evident in the kitchen. A hand gun is located 5 cm from the hand of the man in the kitchen, but no other weapons are recovered inside or outside of the house. Signs of struggle in the house are evident. In the kitchen, two chairs are overturned, and a mug, plate, and fork are on the floor. In the den, several items appear to have been knocked off a bookshelf and a lamp lies broken on its side. A small clump of hair is lying on the carpet near the couch.

You are part of the investigative team assigned to examine and collect evidence at the scene. In this lab, you will design a plan for assessing and collecting evidence at the crime scene using appropriate techniques and tools. Your plan should stress the importance of using precise collecting and handling techniques, and should focus on pieces of evidence you view as crucial in determining events at the scene.

Background

Investigators collect as much relevant evidence as possible at a crime scene. In general, the more evidence collected, the better the odds that some evidence may ultimately be used by prosecutors to make a case. Mistakes made during collection, packaging, and storage can compromise evidence integrity and significance. Procedures and guidelines like the ones given next are followed by crime scene investigators to prevent evidence contamination and loss, increasing evidence value.

General Principles for Evidence Collection and Preservation at the Crime Scene

1. Minimize traffic at the site. Trace evidence can be easily disturbed or contaminated. Contact between investigative personnel and the crime scene should be limited until evidence is secured.

2. Wear protective clothing. Lab coats and disposable gloves can prevent evidence contamination. Change protective gear as necessary to avoid transfer of evidence from one location or piece of evidence to another at a crime scene.
3. Handle evidence sparingly. Handle items as little as possible to minimize loss and contamination.
4. Package items individually. When possible, keep evidence items separated.
5. Use clean equipment and work surfaces. A dirty work surface or tool can contaminate evidence, lessening its potential value.
6. Document evidence. Each item should be tagged with the date/time of collection, name of person who collected it, item description and unique number, and item location.

Collecting Evidence Investigators use various tools and techniques to collect evidence. Once retrieved, it is packaged in clean, dry containers, then sealed to prevent tampering, contamination, or loss.

1. *Picking* – evidence is obtained using forceps.
2. *Lifting* – an adhesive substance like tape is patted/rolled over an item repeatedly, resulting in a transfer of trace evidence.
3. *Scraping* – a spatula is used to scrape evidence from an item.
4. *Vacuum Sweeping* – a vacuum cleaner equipped with a filter trap is used to obtain evidence.
5. *Combing* – a comb or brush is used to recover evidence from a victim's hair.
6. *Clipping* – nail clippers and a file are used to recover evidence on or under fingernails.

Stain Evidence Wet and dry stains can be valuable evidence. The procedures for collecting stains differ.

1. *Wet stains* – soak up stain with sterile cotton tip swabs or clean cotton sheeting. Allow to air dry, then package in clean container.
2. *Dry stains* – moisten sterile cotton tip swabs with distilled water. Rub swabs over stain until substance is picked up. Allow swabs to air dry, then package in a clean container.

Materials

❑ graph paper

Procedure

1. Create a master layout of the crime scene on graph paper. Make it large enough to add the location of key evidence, as well as other notes.
2. Develop a plan for assessing and collecting evidence from the scene. As you work through the plan, think about the following elements:
   - *What items or pieces of evidence should be collected and how?*
   - *What unknown factors must be determined by the evidence?*
   - *Which tasks at the scene have the highest priority?*
   - *How can tasks be divided among team members?*
   - *What learning from previous forensics labs can be applied here?*
3. Share your plan with your teacher and other groups. Based on feedback provided, revise your plan to increase its effectiveness.

Name Date Class

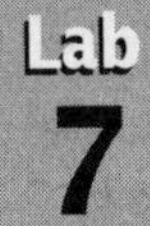

Lab 7 When did she die?

Your medical examiner team has been given the following case to review. It is your job to determine whether the victim died accidentally and what the time of death was. Study the details and complete the medical examiner's report that follows.

The Problem

The victim was found in her home at 10:00 A.M. on Saturday morning by her sister, with whom she was supposed to go jogging. The sister promptly called the police who then notified you, the medical examiner. You noted the following:

- The victim was lying facedown at the bottom of the stairs, facing away from the stairs. The sister indicated the victim was dressed in the clothes she had worn to dinner the night before.
- The victim had no pulse.
- The body was cold to the touch, but the internal temperature, which was measured at 10:30 A.M., was 27°C (room temperature was 20°C).
- Her neck was apparently fractured, and she appeared to have sustained head injuries.
- There were purplish marks on the front of her shoulders and neck; the marks did not change color when touched.
- Her entire body was stiff.
- The victim's eyes were open and cloudy with a thin film.

Additional Police Notes The victim had eaten dinner with her sister at 5:00 P.M. the night before (Friday evening). At dinner, they had agreed to meet at the victim's townhouse at 10:00 A.M. Saturday morning to go jogging. The sister returned to her own home at 11:00 P.M., but she was not sure when the victim returned to her townhouse after dinner. Neighbors did not recall seeing the victim return to her townhouse.

When you performed an autopsy on the victim later that day, you noted that she died of a broken neck and subsequent asphyxiation. The victim was 5 feet 8 inches tall and weighed 130 pounds, her stomach was empty, and her small intestine was full. Your job is to provide police with the time of death.

Background

When a body is discovered, one of the first things that a medical examiner must do is determine the time of death. The medical examiner uses several indicators to help establish the time of death, including body temperature, rigor mortis, discoloration (livor mortis or lividity), and the appearance of the eyes.

Body Temperature When a person dies, the body immediately begins to cool. On average, the body temperature drops at a rate of 0.75°C per hour for the first 12 hours. After 12 hours, the rate of cooling slows by about one half (approximately 0.4°C per hour) until the body reaches ambient temperature, the temperature of the environment. The rate of cooling is also affected by the following factors:

- *Air temperature* – A body will cool faster on a cold winter night than on a warm summer night.
- *Body fat* – Fat tends to insulate the body, so the more fat a person has, the slower the body cools after death.
- *Clothing* – Clothing also insulates the body, so heavy clothing will slow the rate of cooling.
- *Water* – A body in water cools much faster than one in air. Therefore, it is difficult to use body temperature to estimate the time of death for a victim found in the water.

Rigor Mortis At the time of death, the body's muscles are relaxed. However, within 1–2 hours, the muscles begin to stiffen as their stores of adenosine triphosphate (ATP) become exhausted. This stiffening is known as rigor mortis. Rigor mortis begins with the muscles of the face, jaws, and neck, proceeds down the body through the upper arms and torso, and ends with the legs. This process is complete within 8–12 hours after death. As the muscles begin to break down, they begin to relax in the same order as they stiffened. By 24–48 hours after death, the body is totally relaxed again.

Livor Mortis (Lividity) Within 1–2 hours after death, the blood settles into the lowest parts of the body (parts that are closest to or resting on the ground) due to gravity. The red blood cells settle out and break down into the tissues, leaving purplish marks that later become yellow (due to the breakdown of hemoglobin). The color (lividity) becomes fixed in the tissue within 6–8 hours after death. If a body is moved after this time, then the position of the purplish marks may not agree with the position in which the body is found. Finally, if skin appears discolored, but turns white when touched, then lividity has not been fixed and death probably occurred more than 2 hours, but less than 10 hours ago.

Appearance of the Eyes If the eyes remain open at the time of death, then a thin film will appear on them as they begin to dry out. As the blood cells within the body break down, they release potassium. Potassium enters the eyes and causes them to appear cloudy. This process takes approximately 2–3 hours after death; however, if the eyes remain closed after death, then the process takes much longer (approximately 24 hours).

Stomach Contents After you eat, the process of digestion takes place. Digestion begins in the stomach. It takes about 4–6 hours for the stomach to empty its contents into the small intestine. Finally, it takes approximately 12 hours for the food to leave the small intestine. As a rule of thumb:

- Undigested stomach contents—death occurred 0–2 hours after the meal
- Stomach empty—death occurred 4–6 hours after the meal
- Small intestines empty—death occurred 12 hours or more after the meal

Name Date Class

Lab 7

When did she die? *continued*

Materials

- ❑ ruler
- ❑ graph paper
- ❑ your Biology textbook
- ❑ calculator
- ❑ the instructions for this activity

Conclude and Apply

1. What is the normal body temperature in degrees Celsius?

2. What biological process allows humans, mammals, and birds to maintain high body temperatures?

3. Research and explain briefly the role of ATP in muscle contraction.

4. Explain the path that food takes through the digestive system in your body.

5. Based on the background information about the average temperature decrease after death, calculate the body temperature for each hour up to 24 hours after death.

Hour	Body Temp. (C)	Hour	Body Temp. (C)	Hour	Body Temp. (C)
1		9		17	
2		10		18	
3		11		19	
4		12		20	
5		13		21	
6		14		22	
7		15		23	
8		16		24	

Lab 7

When did she die? *continued*

6. Plot the data for temperature versus time after death on graph paper.
7. Based on the body temperature of the victim, how long has it been since the victim died?

8. Estimate the time of death using body temperature.

9. Based on the observations of rigor mortis, how long has the victim been dead?

10. Where was lividity observed on the body? Was it fixed? How long ago did she die? Was the victim found in the position that she died or was her body moved? Explain your answer.

11. Based on the appearance of her eyes, how long ago did she die? Explain your answer.

12. Based on the examination of her digestive system, how long after a meal did the victim die? Explain.

Analyze and Conclude

13. Based on all of the evidence available, estimate the time of death for the victim. Explain your answer.

14. Was the victim's death an accident? Explain your answer.

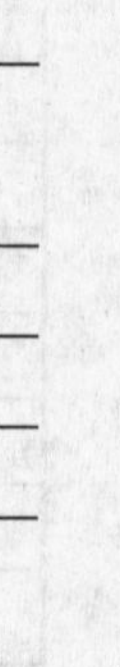

Name Date Class

Lab 8 A Sweet Season

The Problem

The boys' basketball team has been practicing long hours and playing exhausting games all season. Their hard work has paid off. They will be playing in the state championship in two weeks. However, two of the starting players, Jorge and Kyle, have reported to the team doctor. Both boys (age 17) have been complaining about fatigue and muscle weakness and are worried about being able to play their best in the championship.

Listed below are the symptoms the players shared with the doctor.

Jorge: sleepy in classes; muscle weakness; increased appetite; drinks plenty of fluids; occasional dizzy spells after heavy exertion; increased urination (not excessive)

Kyle: sleepy in classes, especially after lunch; muscle weakness; increased appetite, almost excessive; drinks plenty of fluids, but always feels thirsty; frequent dizzy spells after long practices or heavy exertion; urinates frequently; 15 pound weight loss

Both boys had pre-season physical exams and were healthy. However, both boys have a family history of diabetes, a disease in which the body does not effectively respond to the levels of glucose, a very important type of sugar, in the blood. The result is dangerously high concentrations of glucose in the blood. Jorge's father developed diabetes at age 50 and is currently managing it by dieting. Kyle's grandfather had diabetes all of his life. He had to inject insulin daily, developed complications from diabetes, and died at age 55.

Because the symptoms and histories indicate that one or both boys may have diabetes, a glucose tolerance test is ordered to diagnose the disease.

Glucose Tolerance Test On the day of the test, each boy does not eat breakfast. During the test, each boy drinks a concentrated glucose solution (50–100 g glucose) and has blood drawn every 30 minutes for 2.5 hours. The blood samples are spun in a centrifuge to separate plasma from blood cells. A portion of each sample is sent to an outside lab, where the insulin and glucose contents in each plasma sample will be measured.

You are a technician in the lab that will measure the blood glucose by using a glucose test strip. The strip contains an absorbent pad that contains two enzymes, *glucose oxidase* and *peroxidase*, and a color indicator. When a blood sample is applied to the pad, glucose oxidase converts glucose to gluconic acid and hydrogen peroxide. Peroxidase then reacts the hydrogen peroxide with the color indicator, which varies in color from light green to brown depending upon the amount of glucose in the sample. Light green indicates lower glucose concentrations, while dark brown indicates higher concentrations. You will compare the color of the strip to a color scale on the bottle to determine the glucose concentration in the sample. You will then graph and analyze the data to make a preliminary diagnosis.

Name Date Class

Lab 8

A Sweet Season *continued*

Everyday Materials

- ❑ tissues
- ❑ watch with a second hand display or stopwatch
- ❑ ruler
- ❑ graph paper

Lab Materials

- ❑ labeled tubes (12) containing simulated plasma samples (5 mL) from each boy (before, 0.5, 1, 1.5, 2, 2.5 h)
- ❑ glucose test strips (12)
- ❑ copy of the test strip color chart (if you do not have a copy, see the description in the *Procedure*)

Safety

- Never taste or drink anything in the lab.
- Be sure to keep your hands away from your eyes and face in the science lab.
- Wash your hands thoroughly after each lab activity.

Plasma Glucose Concentration (mg/dL)

Time (h)	Jorge	Kyle
Before (0)		
0.5		
1.0		
1.5		
2.0		
2.5		

Test Strip Color Scale

Color	Glucose (mg/dL)
Aqua	<100
Light Green	100
Green	250
Olive	500
Light Brown	1000
Dark Brown	≥ 2000

Procedure

1. To measure glucose in each sample with the test strips, do the following:
   a. Take a strip and hold it by the end opposite the test area.
   b. Dip the strip into the tube containing the sample and remove it immediately (draw the edge of the strip against the rim of the test tube to remove any excess fluid).
   c. Start the stopwatch and compare the color of the strip to the color scale exactly 30 seconds after wetting the strip (ignore any color changes that occur after 30 seconds).
   d. Note the reading on the data table.
   e. Repeat the procedure with the next sample and continue until you have tested all of the samples.
2. On graph paper, plot the data for each boy on the same graph. Plot the plasma glucose concentration on the *y*-axis and time on the *x*-axis.

Use your data to answer the following questions. You may also wish to have your textbook and some additional information about diabetes available.

Conclude and Apply

1. Was the blood glucose concentration the same in each boy prior to the test (i.e. fasting blood glucose)? If not, whose blood glucose concentration was higher?

Name Date Class

2. Describe the changes in blood glucose that occur over time in each boy.

3. How does glucose that you eat get into your bloodstream? In your answer, describe the organs that it must pass through.

4. Does the pattern of the changes in blood glucose that you observed in the boys make sense in light of your answer to question 3? Explain why or why not.

5. Whose blood glucose concentration is more stable (i.e. controlled), Jorge's or Kyle's?

Analyze and Conclude

6. Based on the information that you have so far, do either of the boys have diabetes? If so, which boy and how did you make that conclusion?

7. Obtain a copy of the insulin report from your teacher and look over the data. Describe how insulin levels change with time during the test for each boy.

8. How do the changes in plasma insulin concentration correlate with the changes in blood glucose?

Lab 8 A Sweet Season *continued*

9. Based on the information that you now have, do either of the boys have diabetes? Support your conclusion.

10. Based on your data, what does insulin do to blood glucose levels?

11. Which boy might be better able to withstand a long period without food? Why?

12. If either of the boys has diabetes, explain how the disease accounts for his symptoms. If neither of the boys has diabetes, then what might cause their symptoms? (You will need to obtain information about diabetes.)

13. What treatment might you recommend for each boy? Why?

Name Date Class

Lab 9

Use Blood Types to Help Solve a Crime

The Problem

Some school property was vandalized, and a few drops of blood were found at the scene of the crime. The detectives investigating the incident think that the blood came from the perpetrator of the crime, who apparently was slightly injured during the vandalism. The detectives have gathered a group of suspects who were all on school property when the crime was committed. However, the only hard evidence is the blood found at the scene. In this lab, you will act as a lab technician, analyzing a sample of blood from a suspect to determine the blood type. Each one of your classmates will analyze a sample from a different suspect. Then, you and your classmates will compare the blood types of your samples with the type of blood found at the crime scene in order to narrow down the field of suspects.

Background

Using Blood Typing in Forensics Blood typing is frequently used in forensic investigations. A very small quantity of blood can easily be tested for dozens of genetically controlled traits that have little, if any, environmental influences on their expression. This means that if you know a person's phenotype for these traits, you also know his or her genotype, or genetic identity.

There are hundreds of known human blood-group systems in addition to the familiar ABO and Rh, or rhesus, blood groups. Each system is based on classes of antigenic molecules on the surface of the red blood cells. An antigenic molecule is recognized by the body's immune system as a foreign substance, to which it reacts by producing an antibody. Classification, or typing, of a person's blood to determine which molecular forms are present on the red blood cell depends on antigen-antibody reactions.

Agglutination Reaction If you take serum from a person of known blood type and add it to a drop of blood to be typed, one of two things will happen. The serum may mix freely with the red cells with no noticeable change, or the mixture may agglutinate, that is, the red blood cells clump together, producing a readily observable change as shown in **Figure 1**.

ABO Blood Type There are two common antigenic substances in the ABO blood group, A and B. The O type is not associated with an antigen, which means it is not recognized as a foreign substance by anyone's immune system—even people who do not have O type blood. Antibodies to type A antigen normally are found in the serum of people without the A antigen (that is, in people with type B or type O blood). These anti-A antibodies cause type A cells to agglutinate if they are mixed together. If a blood sample is agglutinated only by anti-A antibodies and not by anti-B antibodies, then the sample is type A, as shown in **Table 1**. Agglutination reactions that identify blood types B, AB, and O also are shown in **Table 1**.

Figure 1

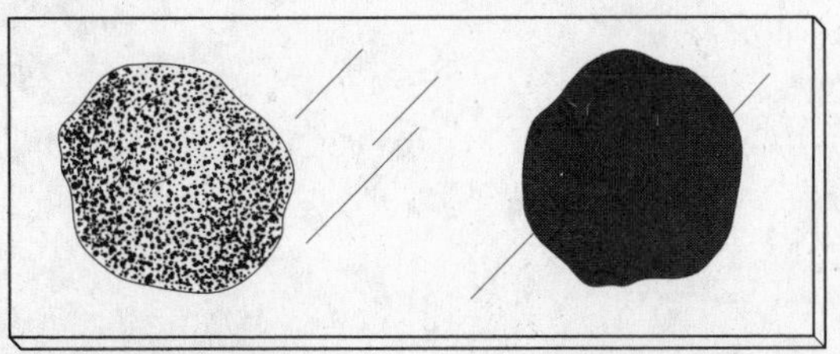

Agglutination (+) *No Agglutination (–)*

Table 1

ABO Blood Type	Anti-A Reaction (+/–)	Anti-B Reaction (+/–)
A	+	–
B	–	+
AB	+	+
O	–	–

Lab 9

Use Blood Types to Help Solve a Crime *continued*

Rhesus Blood Type Rhesus blood types have only one common antigen associated with them. It is often referred to as antigen D. Blood from people with the D antigen (Rh^+) is agglutinated by anti-D antibodies, which may be found in the blood of people without the antigen (Rh^-). Agglutination reactions that identify Rhesus blood types are shown in Table 2.

Table 2

Rhesus Blood Type	Anti-D Reaction (+/–)
Rh^+	+
Rh^-	–

Everyday Materials

- ❑ 10% bleach solution
- ❑ paper towels

Lab Materials

- ❑ ABO/Rh blood-typing test kit (with artificial or aseptic blood samples)
- ❑ protective gloves

Safety

- In this lab, you will work with artificial or aseptic blood samples obtained from your teacher. Handle and dispose of the samples as instructed by the testing kit or your teacher.
- Be sure to keep your hands away from your eyes and face in the science lab.
- Remember to wash your hands thoroughly before and after completing the lab procedure.

Procedure

1. Obtain an ABO/Rh blood-typing test kit from your teacher. Open the kit and assemble the contents for the procedure. Read the kit's instructions.
2. Obtain the blood sample from your teacher. Perform the ABO/Rh test as instructed by the kit. Pay close attention to the amount of time you need to wait for the samples to react.
3. After waiting the time specified in the kit instructions, observe the samples and compare them with **Figure 1**. Record the results, positive or negative for each reaction, in columns 1–3 of **Table 3** under *Data and Observations.*
4. Refer to **Tables 1** and **2** to determine ABO and Rh blood types based on the agglutination reactions. Record the ABO and Rh blood types in column 4 of **Table 3**. Notify your teacher of your results.
5. Dispose of anything with blood on it immediately after use, according to your teacher's instructions.
6. Wipe down your work surface with the bleach solution and paper towels.

Lab 9 Use Blood Types to Help Solve a Crime *continued*

Table 3

1 Anti-A Reaction (+/–)	2 Anti-B Reaction (+/–)	3 Anti-D Reaction (+/–)	4 ABO/Rh Blood Type

Conclude and Apply

1. Your teacher will tell you the number of suspects of each blood type. The type of blood found at the crime scene is A⁺. Based on this information, how many suspects can be ruled out as possible perpetrators of the crime?

2. Explain why blood types can be used only to rule out potential suspects and not to prove conclusively who committed a crime.

3. If you could test for other blood-group types in addition to ABO and Rh, how might this affect the investigation?

Analyze and Conclude

4. All of the ABO/Rh blood types are relatively common in the United States. The most common, O⁺, occurs in 38 percent of people; the least common, AB⁻, occurs in 1 percent of people. A⁺, which was found at the crime scene, occurs in 34 percent of people. Some blood-group systems do not show as much variation, and only a small percentage of people do not have the same blood type. How useful would a less variable blood-group system be for forensic analysis?

Name Date Class

Lab 10 The Missing Restaurant Owner

The Problem

The following is a description of a fictitious murder case. The victim is a restaurant owner who was last known to be at a bus stop approximately 800 meters from his home. He vanished and was never seen again.

Witnesses testified that they heard yelling from the office of the victim's restaurant about the time the victim usually left work for home. Using this testimony, police established the identity of the man the victim was arguing with, and they questioned him as a suspect. The suspect had scratches on his face, which he claimed were from a fight he had the previous evening, and soil particles in his ring and bracelet. The suspect had no explanation for the soil particles or for the reports of yelling from the restaurant office. After arresting the suspect, the police searched his car, the restaurant office, and the surrounding countryside and gathered the following evidence:

List of Evidence

From the suspect's car (trunk):

- Bloodstained watch with the clasp missing (identified as the victim's)
- Strands of hair

From the restaurant office:

- Clasp matching the watch from the suspect's trunk
- Blood samples from the floor

Countryside:

- Bloodstained clothes wrapped in trash bags similar to those used by the restaurant; samples of hair from one of the suspect's dogs and thread from the suspect's sweater found on the clothes
- Knotted electrical cord with hairs that matched those found in the suspect's trunk

The hairs found in the car and on the electrical cord matched samples of the victim's hair taken from his home. Neither the murder weapon nor the body have been found. Your job is to evaluate the forensics evidence and come to a decision about the guilt or innocence of the suspect.

Name Date Class

Part 1

Blood Type Analysis This case is peculiar because there is no body, only hair samples and bloodstains. Whose blood was found? The first thing to do is type the blood samples and then try to identify them.

Three genes (i^A, i^B, i) determine human blood type. Two genes (i^A and i^B) code for two proteins, A and B, that are found on the surface of red blood cells. The i gene does not code for a protein. Because you inherit one gene from your mother and one from your father, there are several possible genotypes and phenotypes (i.e. blood types). If you have one copy of i^A (i^Ai^A or i^Ai), then your red blood cells will have the A protein (blood type A). If you have one copy of i^B (i^Bi^B or i^Bi), then your cells will express the B protein (type B). If you have a copy of i^A and i^B (i^Ai^B), then your cells will express both proteins (type AB). If you only have i genes (ii), then your blood cells will express no protein (type O).

Blood typing is a fast, inexpensive, and easy procedure. To determine blood type, two drops or samples of blood are placed side by side on a glass slide. To one side, a drop of an antibody (anti-A) raised against the A protein is added, while to the other side, a drop of an antibody (anti-B) raised against the B protein is added. If A protein is present on the blood cells, then anti-A will cause them to clump together; likewise anti-B will cause the cells to clump if B protein is present. If no clumping is observed, then neither protein is present.

Procedure

1. Blood type slides from several of the pieces of bloodstained evidence are shown below (anti-A is on the left side and anti-B is on the right side of each slide). The blood-type slide from the suspect is also shown. Because police did not have a blood type for the missing restaurant owner, blood samples were drawn from his parents and are shown as well. Analyze the slides and determine all of the blood types.

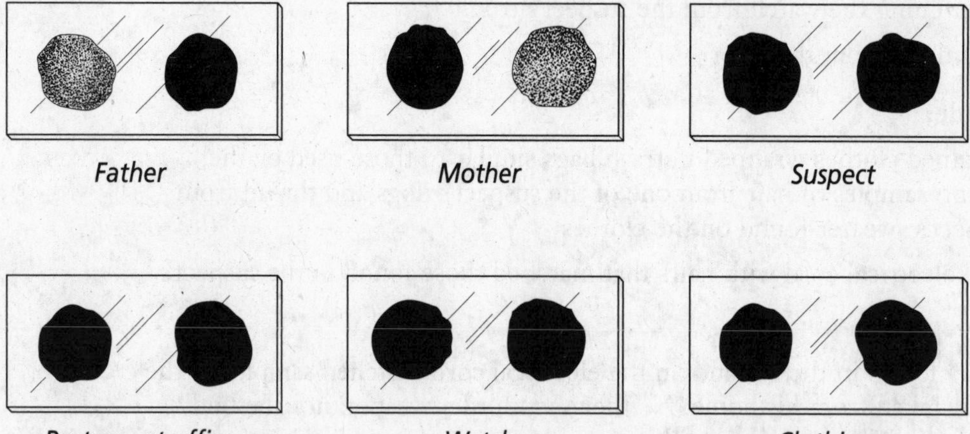

Blood Types:

Father ______ Mother ______ Suspect ______

Clothing ______ Restaurant office ______ Watch ______

Conclude and Apply

1. Is it possible that the blood found in the office and on the clothing was the missing restaurant owner's blood? What was his blood type? Use your knowledge of genetic crosses (i.e., Punnett squares) to determine the victim's possible blood types from the information that you have. Show your work in the space below.

Part 2

DNA-Typing Analysis The blood-typing evidence did not clearly reveal whether the bloodstains belonged to the missing victim. So, investigators turned to a newer technique called DNA fingerprinting or DNA typing. The DNA sequence of human genes (DNA that codes for proteins) follows fairly regular patterns; however, the DNA sequences between genes (i.e. non-coding DNA) differ greatly among individuals. Scientists understand how to identify and analyze these special sequences, so they can tell if two DNA samples probably came from the same person. Since DNA is inherited from each parent, an individual shares patterns within these sequences with his or her parents. Therefore, scientists can also tell whether or not two samples came from individuals who are related.

To conduct a DNA typing experiment, traces of DNA are collected from an individual or crime scene. Then, a technique called polymerase chain reaction (PCR) is used to make copies of the DNA to increase the amount. PCR enables analyzable DNA to be obtained from extremely small samples. The DNA is then cut into fragments using specific enzymes called restriction enzymes. The fragments, which are of different sizes, are separated using a technique called gel electrophoresis. The pattern of separated DNA fragments are transferred from the gel to a piece of filter paper and mixed with radioactive segments of DNA that correspond to an individual's unique sequences. After exposing the filter paper to the radioactive compounds, it is dried and exposed to X-ray film; the fragments containing an individual's unique sequences will show up as dark bands on the film. Now you have a DNA fingerprint. In practice, many DNA samples are loaded on the gel for comparison.

DNA typing compares the bands from a known sample to those of suspects. The bands from two different samples will match only if the same individual donated both samples. Even though an individual's pattern of bands is unique, children will share bands with both parents.

To verify the identity of the victim, DNA typing was done using samples of DNA from his mother (A), father (B), the suspect (C), the watch (D), the restaurant office (E), and the clothing (F). Read the gels on the next page from top to bottom and compare the columns.

Name Date Class

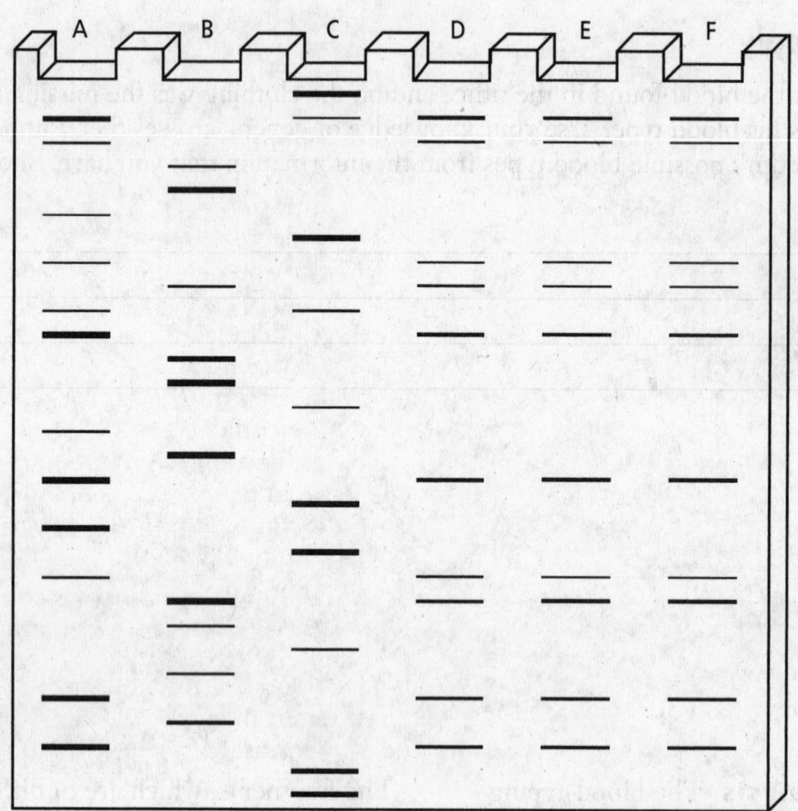

2. Was the victim genetically related to the mother and father tested in columns A and B? Explain your answer.

3. Given that there was no body or murder weapon found, do you think that the evidence indicates beyond a reasonable doubt that the suspect murdered the victim? Explain your answer.

Analyze and Conclude

4. Form groups of four students. Two students should act as prosecutors while the other two act as defense attorneys. Each pair should prepare an argument explaining why the suspect is guilty (prosecution) or innocent (defense). Use the lines below to list ideas you will use in your argument.

Teacher Guide and Answers

Lab 1 ▪ Where did they drown?

Purpose

In this activity, students will learn about diffusion and osmosis and apply this knowledge to determine where two bodies found in a bay drowned and determine whether they were the victims of accidental drowning or murder.

Biological Concepts

Have students review the following concepts before beginning this activity:

- ❑ diffusion
- ❑ osmosis
- ❑ selected permeabilty

Time

1 hour

Teaching Tips

- This activity should be done with groups of three students.
- Sugar from the grocery store is cheaper and can be used in place of lab-grade sucrose.

Background

The students place 10% sucrose in dialysis bags and place the bags in various solutions [1% (A), 5% (B), 10% (C), 20% (D), and 40% (E)]. Note that Beakers A–E are set up to give students practice understanding osmosis and osmotic pressure. Beakers F and G represent the circumstances of the drowning victims, with the solutions inside the bags representing the water in the lungs (fresh or salt), and the solutions in the beakers representing the victims' blood. Students should measure the changes in weight of the bags after 30 min. Solutions in Beakers A and B are hypotonic relative to the bags, so water will flow from the solutions into the bags and increase the weights of Bags A and B (A > B). Beaker C is isotonic relative to the bag, so flow across the membrane should be equal in both directions and there should be no significant change in the weight of Bag C. Beakers D and E are hypertonic relative to the bags, so water should flow from the bags into the solutions and decrease the weights of Bags D and E (D < E).

Beaker F represents a victim who drowned in freshwater, as explained in the lab. The 1% sucrose in the bag is hypotonic relative to the 10% solution in the beaker. Water should flow from the bag into the beaker, and the bag will lose weight. Consequently, the concentration of sucrose in the bag will increase, and the concentration of sucrose in the beaker (blood) should decrease. In contrast, Beaker G represents a victim who drowned in salt water, as explained in the lab. The 40% sucrose in the bag is hypertonic relative to the 10% solution in the beaker. Water should flow from the beaker into the bag, and the bag will gain weight. Consequently, the concentration of sucrose in the bag will decrease, and the concentration of sucrose in the beaker (blood) should increase.

Students will use the hypothetical blood concentration data of the drowning victims to determine whether the victims drowned in freshwater or salt water. The concentrations of sodium, potassium, and chloride increased in the man's blood, which indicates that he drowned in salt water. In contrast, the concentrations of these ions decreased in the woman's blood, which indicates that she drowned in freshwater. Encourage students to discuss different ways a victim who drowned in freshwater could end up in salt water and to discuss any other evidence that might help determine whether the deaths were murders or accidents.

Advance Preparation

1. On the day before the lab, cut the dialysis tubing into sections and soak in water.
2. On the day before the lab, prepare the sucrose solutions. You can refrigerate the solutions overnight, but warm them to room temperature prior to use. Make 4.3 L of 40% sucrose stock solution by dissolving 1.72 kg sucrose in 4.3 L of water. Make dilutions of the stock solution to yield the following sucrose solutions in the table below:

Sucrose Concentration %	40% Sucrose (mL)	Water (mL)	Total (mL)
1	50	1950	2000
5	250	1750	2000
10	1000	3000	4000
20	1000	1000	2000

Lab 1 ▪ Where did they drown? *continued*

Answers

1. The masses of Bags A and B should increase. The mass gain of Bag A should be greater than that of Bag B.
2. The concentrations of Beakers A and B were less than the concentrations inside the bags. You would classify them as hypotonic relative to the bags.
3. The concentrations of sucrose inside Bags A and B were greater than the surrounding solutions. Therefore, the water concentrations inside the bags were less than those in the surrounding solutions. Water diffused from the beakers (high concentration) into the bags (low concentration), thereby increasing the masses of the bags. The difference in the water concentration across the bag was greater in Bag A than in Bag B. Therefore, Bag A had more water diffused into it and showed a greater mass gain than Bag B.
4. The mass of Bag C should not change.
5. The concentration of sucrose inside Bag C was the same as the concentration of sucrose in the beaker. Therefore, Bag C was isotonic compared to the surrounding solution.
6. Because the concentrations of sucrose inside and outside Bag C were the same, there was no difference in the concentration of water across the bag. Therefore, the diffusion of water across the membrane was equal in both directions, and the mass of Bag C did not change.
7. The masses of Bags D and E should decrease. The mass loss of Bag E should be greater than that of Bag D.
8. The concentrations of Beakers D and E were greater than the concentrations inside the bags. You would classify them as hypertonic relative to the bags.
9. The concentrations of sucrose inside Bags D and E were less than the surrounding solutions. Therefore, the water concentrations inside the bags were greater than those in the surrounding solutions. Water diffused from the bags (high concentration) into the beakers (low concentration), thereby decreasing the masses of the bags. The difference in the water concentration across the bag was greater in Bag E than in Bag D. Therefore, Bag E had more water diffusing out of it and showed a greater loss of mass than Bag D.
10. The bag should lose mass, which indicates that water moved out of the bag. The concentration of sucrose in the beaker, which represents the salts in the blood, was greater than inside the bag, which represents the salt concentration in the freshwater in the lungs. Therefore, the concentration of water inside the bag was greater than the surrounding solution. Water diffused out of the bag and diluted the contents of the surrounding solution. So, the concentration of sucrose in the beaker should decrease.
11. The bag should gain weight, which indicates that water moved into the bag. The concentration of sucrose in the beaker, which represents the salts in the blood, was less than inside the bag, which represents the salt concentration in the salt water in the lungs; therefore, the concentration of water inside the bag was less than the surrounding solution. Water diffused into the bag. The loss of water from the beaker solution increased the sucrose concentration in the beaker.
12. The increased salt concentration of the man's blood indicated that he drowned in salt water, possibly the San Francisco Bay, much like the situation in Beaker G. In contrast, the salt concentration in the woman's blood indicated that she drowned in freshwater, much like the situation in Beaker F.
13. Because the data indicate that the man drowned in salt water, it is possible that he drowned in the San Francisco Bay and that his death could have been an accident. Other evidence would be needed to determine that his death was not an accident. Because the data indicate that the woman drowned in freshwater, it seems likely that the woman was drowned elsewhere and her body was dumped into the bay as a result of a murder. However, you might also conclude that she drowned in a river or freshwater tributary of the bay and was washed into the San Francisco Bay prior to her discovery.

Lab 2 ▪ Can fingerprint analysis connect a suspect to a crime scene?

Purpose

In this activity, students will investigate characteristics of friction ridge patterns in skin. They will use specific characteristics, as well as an understanding of the underlying principles of fingerprint identification, to determine the existence of a match among several fingerprint impressions.

Biological Concepts

Have students review the following concepts before beginning this activity:

❑ integumentary system components and function
❑ dermal and epidermal properties and structure
❑ oil and sweat glands
❑ skin elasticity

Expected Outcome

Students will determine a match between two fingerprints based on friction ridge patterns and characteristics.

Time

45–50 minutes

Instructor's Materials List

❑ ink pad
❑ index cards
❑ photocopies of fingerprints labeled as follows: *Suspect A Fingerprint*, *Suspect B Fingerprint*, and *Unidentified Fingerprint* (one of each per group of two students)
❑ microscopes/magnifying lenses

Advance Preparation

1. Obtain Suspect A's fingerprint by lightly pressing a volunteer's thumb to the surface of an ink pad, rolling the thumb from left to right across an index card, then immediately lifting the thumb straight up from the card.
2. Obtain Suspect B's fingerprint and the Unidentified Fingerprint using the same procedure. ***To ensure a match, one of the suspect's fingerprints should be obtained from the same person who supplies the unidentified fingerprint.***
3. Make a photocopy of each fingerprint, enlarging the image if possible.
4. Label each fingerprint as *Suspect A Fingerprint*, *Suspect B Fingerprint*, or *Unidentified Fingerprint*. Make enough copies of the fingerprints for each group.
5. Take your time when creating fingerprint samples—multiple attempts might be needed to obtain favorable results.

Teaching Strategies

- Reinforce the connection between the structure and function of friction ridge skin in providing a gripping surface for fingers and toes.
- Discuss similarities and differences among friction ridge characteristics. Inform students that some fingerprint experts classify characteristics as either ridge endings or bifurcations, with all other categories being combinations of these.
- Students might be interested in analyzing their own fingerprints after completing this exercise. Maximize this interest by having students compare one fingerprint from each hand. This will reinforce how the tremendous variability in friction ridge characteristics translates into differences in ridge patterns, even within one individual.

Teaching Tips

- Divide the class into pairs to work on this activity.
- Enlarging fingerprints during photocopying will allow students to label and compare friction ridge characteristics more easily.
- Make microscopes or magnifying lenses available for students who are interested in viewing the original fingerprints or copies in greater detail.

Lab 2 ▪ Can fingerprint analysis connect a suspect to a crime scene? *continued*

Background

Fingerprinting has been used in various countries for over 100 years. Because of the random manner of friction ridge skin formation during in utero development, scientists believe sufficient variability exists to ensure no two humans have identical friction ridge patterns. While impossible to prove conclusively, there is evidence to support this hypothesis. Studies have demonstrated that while identical twins share the same DNA profile markers, their fingerprints always show variation. In addition, no identical fingerprints have, to date, been identified in worldwide databases, like the FBI's Integrated Automated Fingerprint Identification System (IAFIS), which collectively hold hundreds of millions of fingerprints. The IAFIS maintains the largest biometric database in the world, containing fingerprints and criminal history information for more than 47 million subjects.

One drawback inherent in using fingerprints to link an individual to a location or object lies in the fact that the age of a set of fingerprints is almost impossible to determine. While a fingerprint can help prove an individual was at a crime scene, the fingerprint alone does not provide information about when the individual was at the location. Furthermore, there is nothing in fingerprint variation to allow a prediction of the gender or race of the subject.

Answers

1. Answers will vary. Students should find at least ten points of similarity between one of the suspect's fingerprints and the unidentified fingerprint. While students should find at least one point of dissimilarity between one of the suspect's fingerprints and the unidentified fingerprint, they might also find some points of similarity.
2. Students should determine a match between one of the suspect's fingerprints and the unidentified fingerprint. Justification for the match is based on finding at least 10 points of similarity between the two impressions.
3. The presence of the suspect's fingerprint on the tenth-floor office proves that the suspect was lying about having been at the crime scene. While answers about confidence will vary, they should relate to student comfort level in comparing friction ridge characteristics.
4. Human skin is elastic. Factors affecting precise fingerprint measurements include the force with which the impression is made and changes in the size of the finger.
5. Answers will vary. The more points of similarity, the better the match. In determining possible criminal action which carries consequences of the law, law-enforcement officers work to be as certain of a match as possible.

Lab 3 ▪ The Importance of Trace Evidence in Forensic Science

Purpose

In this activity, students will investigate trace evidence, specifically focusing on fiber and hair samples. Based on the data, students will determine the possibility of contact between the victim and an identified suspect on the night of the murder.

Biological Concepts

Have students review the following concepts before beginning this activity:

- ❑ hair shaft structure
- ❑ properties of the cuticle, cortex, medulla
- ❑ use of a compound light microscope

Expected Outcome

Students will compare trace evidence and conclude that consistencies among samples support, but cannot prove, that contact between the victim and an identified suspect took place on the night of the murder.

Time

50 minutes

Teacher Guide and Answers

Lab 3 ▪ The Importance of Trace Evidence in Forensic Science *continued*

Advance Preparation

1. Obtain fiber samples from various textiles, like cotton, wool, rayon, and polyester. Sources can include clothing, furniture, bedding, and carpeting. Put samples in petri dishes or other covered flat containers which allow easy access with forceps. Containers should be clearly labeled with the type and/or source of the fiber.
2. Provide appropriate hair samples with as much variety as possible. Sources can include, but are not limited to, humans, cats, and dogs. Put samples in petri dishes or other covered flat containers which allow easy access with forceps. Containers should be clearly labeled with the hair source.
3. Prepare and clearly label multiple slides of each of the following:
   Fiber A, Victim's clothing: Fiber from either a car floor mat or carpet from a car trunk. Note: Fibers A and B should have the same source.
   Fiber B, Victim's clothing: Fiber from either a car floor mat or carpet from a car trunk. Note: Fibers A and B should have the same source.
   Fiber C, Suspect's car: Fiber with characteristics that do not match Fibers A and B.
   Fiber D, Suspect's car: Fiber from either a car floor mat or carpet from a car trunk. Note: Fiber D should have the same source as Fibers A and B.
   Hair A, Found between victim's fingers: Human head hair. Note: Hairs A and C should have the same source.
   Hair B, Victim's sweatshirt: Human head hair. Note: Hairs B and D should have the same source.
   Hair C, Suspect: Human head hair. Note: Hairs A and C should have the same source.
   Hair D, Victim: Human head hair. Note: Hairs B and D should have the same source.
4. Be sensitive to cultural factors in your community as you select hair samples for student analysis.

Teaching Strategies

- Explain that because different hairs on the same person can show many variations, investigators collect multiple hairs for comparison if possible. An average sample ranges from 24 to 50 pieces and is typically collected from several different parts of the body as well as various areas of the scalp.
- Have students brainstorm other types of biological trace evidence that might be found at a crime scene.
- Circulate throughout the lab to answer questions while students are examining hair and fiber samples.

Teaching Tips

- Review the preparation of a wet-mount slide prior to beginning the lab.
- Review how to examine objects using several different magnification powers on a compound light microscope prior to beginning the lab.
- Groups of two or three students are optimal.

Background

Hairs of mammals are composed primarily of the protein alpha-keratin. Hair of different mammal species varies in characteristics like length, color, shape, root appearance, and internal microscopic features. A great deal of variability exists among hairs found on a single animal. In humans, hairs found on the head, pubic region, arms, legs, and other body areas have specific characteristics that can determine their origin.

A variety of factors can affect the transfer of trace evidence, such as hair and textile fibers, from a suspect to a victim. The duration and force of contact, the ability of the victim to move after the crime occurs, and the length of time between actual physical contact and collection of clothing items will impact the amount of trace evidence that remains for investigation.

Lab 3 ▪ The Importance of Trace Evidence in Forensic Science *continued*

Answers

1. Fibers A and B should share similar characteristics. They should be consistent with either Fiber C or Fiber D, depending on how the evidence is structured. Characteristics might include fiber type, color, amount of twist, fineness/coarseness, pits, striations, shape, and relative width.
2. Depending on how the trace evidence is structured, students might believe the victim was either lying on floor mats on the floor of the car or in the trunk of the car.
3. Hair samples A and C, found between the victim's fingers and taken from the suspect's head, should have similar features. Hair samples B and D, found on the victim's sweatshirt and taken from the victim's head, should have similar features.
4. Yes; hair samples found between the victim's fingers are consistent with hair from the suspect's head.
5. No; investigators can only conclude that fibers on the victim's clothing are consistent with fibers present in the suspect's car, and that hair found between the victim's fingers is consistent with the suspect's hair.
6. Answers will vary. Listed events might include the victim leaving the dorm room for a jog, being approached by the suspect, forced to get into the car, attacked and strangled, and the body left in the wooded area.
7. Answers will vary but might include eyewitnesses, suspect motive, placement of suspect with victim prior to death, presence of suspect's fingerprints at the scene or on the body, and presence of suspect's DNA on the victim's body.
8. Answers will vary. Students might have accidentally included samples of their own hair, or might have incorrectly labeled samples.

Lab 4 ▪ Can insect evidence establish time of death?

Purpose

In this activity, students will use insect evidence and other data to estimate time of death of a victim.

Biological Concepts

- ❑ arthropod physiology
- ❑ arthropod reproduction
- ❑ arthropod metamorphosis

Expected Outcome

Students will use crime scene data and graphs illustrating relationships among temperature, blow fly development stage, and larval size to estimate time of death.

Time

50 minutes

Teaching Strategies

- Review the stages of blow fly development using **Figure 1.** Reinforce the connection between each stage and its instar definition. Note: Adult flies are constantly coming to the body, so aging depends on the development of eggs and larvae from the initial visits.
- Have students confirm their calculations of average temperature with you before proceeding. The estimation of time of death depends on a correct calculation.
- Discuss how the fluctuating temperature of an outdoor environment adds uncertainty to the estimation of time of death. Have students compare the effect of this uncertainty during various months of the year in their geographic location, as well as others.

Teaching Tips

- This activity can be done individually or in groups of two.

Teacher Guide and Answers

Lab 4 ▪ Can insect evidence establish time of death? *continued*

- Use of a ruler when reading graphs will lead to a more accurate interpretation of graphed data.
- If possible, be available to field questions students might encounter when working through the *Conclude and Apply* and *Analyze and Conclude* sections of the lab.

Background

After 48 to 72 hours after death, forensic entomology is sometimes the only method for determining the amount of time that has passed since death. If the time frame is relatively short, entomologists can base an estimate of time of death on the stage of development of a single insect species which initially colonizes the body. This is the strategy students use to analyze data in this activity. Once these insects have reached maturity, however, another approach must be used. In these cases, forensic entomologists can often analyze data from successive waves of different insects that inhabit a human corpse over time. Some insects, like blow flies, arrive on a corpse almost immediately, while others are more attracted to a body in advanced stages of decay. This natural insect succession is known and can help an entomologist establish time elapsed since death for up to a year. In addition to providing clues about time of death, insects can sometimes help establish if a corpse has been moved or disturbed after death and can provide clues about the presence and position of wounds that might be obscured by decomposition.

Forensic entomology has limitations, however. In some locations, insects are only abundant during certain seasons of the year. In other cases, a body might be deeply buried or wrapped tightly in some material, preventing insects from reaching it. In addition, forensic entomology is an emerging area of forensic science. Though their numbers are growing, forensic entomology experts are not widely available for consultation during investigations.

Answers

1. The medical examiner noted large maggots moving away from the corpse, an indicator that they were in the third instar stage of development. At the average temperature calculated, this would have made the larvae between six and nine days old. The woman had only been missing for eight days, which narrowed time of death to between six and eights days prior to the discovery of the body.
2. The body was left at the scene on October 3—six days prior to its discovery. This estimate is based on the length of the larvae, the average temperature at the scene, and the date the body was discovered.
3. The victim was murdered on the evening of October 2 or in the early hours of October 3. The victim was last seen alive on October 2, and entomological evidence shows the victim had been at the scene for roughly six days.
4. Yes; if the body was placed in a car or car trunk for some period of time before being taken to the site, insects might not have been able to access it immediately after death. It is possible that the body was wrapped tightly in some material prior to being taken to the site, also limiting insect exposure. Given that the victim was last seen alive on October 2, however, the amount of time between the murder and the body being deposited at the scene was limited.
5. While temperature is the primary climatological factor affecting blow fly development, factors including cloud cover, rainfall, wind, and humidity could have played secondary roles in the rate of development. In addition, time of death in this case is based on the average temperature for the time period, which could affect the estimate to some degree.
6. Answers will vary. The entomological evidence establishes a time line of events and suggests that the victim died shortly after the time she was seen with the suspect. Combined with hair, fiber, and other evidence, it might help strengthen the case against the suspect.

Lab 5 ▪ Forensic Odontology at Work

Purpose

The purpose of this lab is to demonstrate how characteristics of a dental impression in a food item are compared to a known exemplar to determine the likelihood of a match.

Biological Concepts

Have students review the following concepts before beginning this activity:

- ❑ mechanical digestion
- ❑ tooth characteristics and structure
- ❑ mouth components and structure

Expected Outcome

Students should determine a match between the dental impression left in a food item and a polystyrene dental impression made by a known individual.

Time

50 minutes

Advance Preparation

- Secure a volunteer willing to create dental impressions. The impressions will be made in blocks of cheddar cheese and polystyrene plates. Consider having a second volunteer create a polystyrene dental impression. Then run the lab with two suspects, one who is a positive match with the cheese impression and one who is not a match.
- Create the dental impression in the food item: Have the "suspect" take a bite out of the cheese block. It is likely that only the front teeth, both top and bottom, will appear in the impression. However, the more teeth present in the food item impression, the more likely students will be able to make a positive identification. Use an anti-bacterial wipe to remove any saliva apparent on the cheese. Repeat for the appropriate number of groups.
- Create the dental impression in polystyrene: Cut a polystyrene plate into six wedges. Stack two of the wedges together, and cut off about three centimeters of the pointed ends of the wedges. Wipe the polystyrene surface with an antibacterial wipe. Place the two wedges into the "suspect's" mouth until as many teeth are touching the plate pieces as possible. Have the volunteer bite down firmly on the wedges, then remove them. Use an antibacterial wipe to remove any saliva apparent on the plates, then label the top and bottom wedges. Repeat for the appropriate number of groups.

Teaching Strategies

- To ensure understanding of the variability inherent in dentition, ask students to create a simple written record of their own dentition, then compare it to others in the class. By examining their teeth using a mirror, students can note characteristics including gaps, fillings, twisted or missing teeth, missing or removed molars, or other unusual features.
- Describe how the "suspect's" polystyrene dental impressions were created.
- Talk with students about the importance of handling the food item with care. Dropping or crushing any part of the food could result in changes in the impression.

Teaching Tips

- Teeth models might be costly. Have students handle teeth models with care. Inquire with your school's health teacher about borrowing a model, if available.
- Insist that student work carefully through steps 1-3 in the *Procedure* section. While students will be interested in comparing impressions to make an identification, the initial steps of the lab lay an important foundation for the comparison process.
- If few teeth models are available, have students complete steps 1-2 in the *Procedure* section in larger groups, then divide students into smaller groups to complete the rest of the lab.

Lab 5 ▪ Forensic Odontology at Work
continued

Background

The work of a forensic odontologist covers a variety of areas, including
- identification of bite marks on assault victims;
- comparison of bite marks with the teeth of a suspect and presentation of this evidence in court as an expert witness;
- identification of bite marks in materials like wood, leather and food items;
- identification of unknown bodies through dental records;
- age estimations of skeletal remains.

A forensic odontologist might be called upon to analyze bite marks on the body of an assault victim. Bite-mark evidence on skin is typically two-dimensional, which can make it more difficult to analyze than an impression found in certain food items. While a bite might penetrate the skin, it often leaves only bruising. The blood marks of a bruise can also be mistaken for the impression of a tooth. Bite marks left in food items can offer a three-dimensional view, increasing their value for comparison to an individual's dentition.

Answers

1. A match was established between the suspect's dental impression and the impression in the cheese block.
2. Answers will vary but might include gaps between teeth, twisted or rotated teeth, or teeth with unusual surfaces. Teeth that leave the strongest impressions are generally in the front, both top and bottom, making it likely that these were most useful in the comparison.
3. Answers will vary. The more unique or distinctive the characteristics of the teeth used to create the impressions, the greater the likelihood that students will feel confident in the analysis.
4. Among other arguments, a defense attorney might argue that changes in the cheese resulting from improper handling or decay could have altered the impression in the food.
5. Investigators might search for evidence including fingerprints, footprints, hair or fiber samples, or any body fluids that potentially yield a DNA sample. They would also seek potential witnesses to the crime to provide information about the perpetrator's physical appearance.

Lab 6 ▪ Crime Scene Investigation

Purpose

The purpose of this activity is to give students the opportunity to apply learning from previous forensics labs, as well as information related to evidence collection, to formulate a plan for collecting and assessing evidence from a crime scene.

Biological Concepts

Biological concepts addressed in previous forensics labs in this manual should be reviewed as necessary.

Expected Outcome

Students should create a plan which outlines the tools, techniques, and overall strategy they would use to collect and assess evidence at a crime scene. Based on feedback, they should revise plans to increase their effectiveness.

Time

one class period to develop the plan
one to two class periods to share, critique, and revise plans

Teaching Strategies

- Review key concepts from previous forensics labs before beginning this lab. Encourage students to apply what they have learned in these labs when developing their plans.
- As students are developing their plans, encourage them to
  - make a list of the evidence present at the crime scene;
  - list how the evidence will be collected and packaged;
  - decide what types of analyses should be done on the evidence collected;

Lab 6 ▪ Crime Scene Investigation *continued*

- consider evidence that might be located somewhere other than the crime scene that might shed light on what happened;
- develop a list of questions investigators might have about what happened at the scene;
- list and prioritize the tasks that need to be accomplished regarding collection and analysis of evidence.

- Once groups have developed and shared their plans, have students complete a rubric to evaluate their own plans, as well as other groups' plans. Consider sharing the rubric with students as they develop their plans, providing a standard for comparison.

Teaching Tips

- Groups of three or four work well for this activity.
- Consider having students use a computer program with basic drawing features to generate a layout of the crime scene.
- Provide access to previously completed forensics labs as resource material.

Background

Crime-scene technicians, law-enforcement officers, medical personnel, and others who investigate crime scenes are trained to use special techniques for locating, collecting, and preserving evidence. Investigators use a variety of methods for detecting evidence, including general visual searches, visual searches assisted by special illumination like ultraviolet and laser light, and visual searches assisted by magnification. Once evidence is detected, there are a variety of methods for collecting it. Regardless of the method used, investigators follow the general rule that recovery techniques should be the most direct and least intrusive possible.

Proper packaging of evidence is critical in maintaining its value. Wet evidence must be dried to prevent destruction by fungal growth. Packages must be sealed to prevent tampering, loss of evidence, or contamination of evidence from an outside source.

Evaluation Rubric

Utilize this rubric to evaluate plans and provide feedback.

Crime Scene Investigation Plan	Points Possible	Self-Assessment OR Assessment of Another Plan	Teacher Assessment
The plan provides a list of evidence that will be collected.	10		
The plan outlines procedures for collecting specific evidence.	10		
The plan lists questions investigators haveabout events at the crime scene.	10		
The plan lists tasks that must be accomplished at the scene in priority order.	10		
The plan accounts for division of labor among team members.	10		

Use the following rating scale:

Excellent: 9-10 points, **Very Good:** 7-8 points, **Good:** 5-6 points, **Satisfactory**: 3-4 points, **Poor**: 1-2 points, **Unsatisfactory**: 0 points

Teacher Guide and Answers

Lab 7 ▪ When did she die?

Purpose

In this activity, students will play the role of a medical examiner and use various biological data (e.g., body temperature, rigor mortis, livor mortis, eye appearance, stomach contents) to determine the time of death of a victim.

Biological Concepts

Have students review the following concepts before beginning this activity:

- ❑ human physiology
- ❑ pathology
- ❑ ATP in muscle contractions
- ❑ digestion

Expected Outcome

Students will examine crime scene and autopsy evidence to determine when the victim died.

Time

30–45 minutes

Teaching Tips

- The activity can be done individually or in groups of two.
- You might want to entertain a debate or discussion about the circumstances surrounding the death.
- You might want to bring in a medical examiner or a member of a police forensics team to discuss his or her job with the students and the use of biology in crime-solving.
- Students could use a final report format similar to a medical examiner's report instead of the traditional questions and answers.

Background

The victim was found lying facedown at the bottom of the stairs in her townhouse. From the temperature of her body (27°C), students will be able to estimate that she died 11.5 hours before, or at 11:00 P.M. the previous night. Her body was in complete rigor mortis, which is consistent with the estimated time of death from body temperature measurements. Her body showed fixed lividity on the shoulders and neck; these marks were not inconsistent with a fall down the stairs. Her stomach was empty, but her small intestine had food in it, which indicates that she died at least 4–6 hours after eating. This finding is consistent with the 5:00 P.M. dinner with her sister. Her eyes were cloudy, which indicates that death occured at least 2–3 hours before.

Students might speculate that the victim died at approximately 11:00 P.M. the night before. She must have eaten dinner at least 4–6 hours before death. She died of a broken neck and the scene might suggest that it was an accidental death when she fell down the steps after returning home late Friday evening.

Answers

1. The normal body temperature is 37°C.
2. The breakdown of foods (i.e., metabolism) provides the heat energy necessary for humans, mammals, and birds to maintain their body temperatures above the temperature of their surroundings.
3. To contract, the myosin filaments form chemical bonds called crossbridges. These crossbridges are repeatedly formed and broken as a muscle contracts. ATP is required to break the crossbridges. When ATP is no longer present (i.e., after death), the crossbridges form and muscles contract, but cannot relax. Within about 24–48 hours, the proteins in the muscles begin to decompose, and the effects of rigor mortis lessen.
4. Food enters your body through your mouth and, when you swallow, continues down your esophagus into your stomach. After the food is digested in your stomach, it proceeds into the small intestine, where most of the nutrients are absorbed. From the small intestine, the food passes into the large intestine, where water is absorbed and feces are formed and stored in the rectum. The feces leave the rectum through the anus.

Teacher Guide and Answers

Lab 7 ▪ When did she die? *continued*

5.

Hour	Body Temp. (C)	Hour	Body Temp. (C)	Hour	Body Temp. (C)
1	36.2	9	29.5	17	24.9
2	35.3	10	28.7	18	24.5
3	34.5	11	27.8	19	24.1
4	33.7	12	27	20	23.7
5	32.8	13	26.6	21	23.3
6	32	14	26.2	22	22.8
7	31.2	15	25.8	23	22.4
8	30.3	16	25.3	24	22

6.

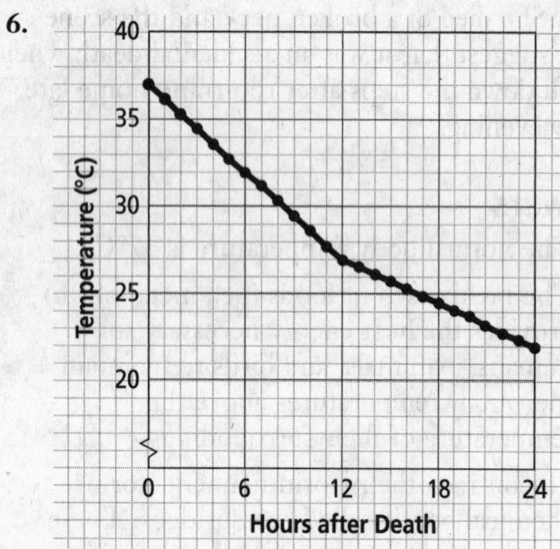

7. The victim's body temperature was 27°C, which would indicate that she had been dead approximately 11.5 hours.

8. Since her body temperature was measured at 10:30 A.M., she probably died at approximately 11:00 P.M. the previous night.

9. Because the body was in complete rigor mortis, which takes approximately 8–12 hours, the victim must have been dead at least 8–12 hours, but less than 24–48 hours—the time frame in which the body relaxes again.

10. Lividity was observed on the front of her shoulders and neck and was fixed. Because lividity was fixed, she must have been dead at least 6–8 hours. The victim was found lying face down, so the lividity marks are consistent with the position in which the body was found.

11. The victim must have died with her eyes open because they were cloudy and a thin film had developed. She must have been dead at least 2–3 hours.

12. It takes approximately 4–6 hours for the stomach to empty into the small intestine. The victim's stomach was empty, but her small intestine contained food, which indicates that she must have died at least 4–6 hours after she had eaten her last meal.

13. The victim was found lying facedown at the bottom of the stairs in her townhouse. From the temperature of her body (27°C), she died 11.5 hours before, or at approximately 11:00 P.M. the previous night. Her body was in complete rigor mortis, which is consistent with the estimated time of death from body temperature measurements because complete rigor mortis occurs 8–12 hours after death. Her stomach was empty, but her small intestine had food in it, which indicates that she died at least 4–6 hours after eating. Her eyes were cloudy, which indicates that death occurred at least 2–3 hours before. Overall, the evidence is consistent with an estimate of 11:00 P.M. for time of death.

14. The victim died at approximately 11:00 P.M. the night before. The scene suggests that it was an accidental death when she fell down the steps after returning home late Friday evening. The death was probably accidental.

Teacher Guide and Answers

Lab 8 ▪ A Sweet Season

Purpose

In this activity, students will measure glucose in simulated plasma samples, plot data for a glucose tolerance test, diagnose two hypothetical patients for possible diabetes, and learn about diabetes and glucose metabolism.

Biological Concepts

Have students review the following concepts before beginning this activity:

- ❑ diabetes
- ❑ digestive system
- ❑ glucose in the bloodstream
- ❑ insulin

Expected Outcome

Students will simulate a blood glucose test and diagnose diabetes in the patients.

Time

30–45 minutes

Instructor's Materials List

- ❑ glucose solutions made from glucose tablets (5 g per tablet, Becton-Dickinson, available from local pharmacy)
- ❑ distilled water
- ❑ four reagent bottles with caps (500 mL)
- ❑ Diastix™ Reagent test strips for Urinalysis (Bayer Corporation, available from local pharmacy), 12 per group
- ❑ plastic or glass test tubes with caps (5–10 mL capacity)
- ❑ test-tube rack, one per group
- ❑ stopwatch or other watch with a second hand, one per group
- ❑ tissues to wipe excess fluid
- ❑ ruler, one per student

Advance Preparation

(for a class of 30 students, 15 groups of 2)

1. Make 1 L of 1000 mg/dL (10 g/L) stock solution by dissolving two glucose tablets in 1 L of distilled water. Label this solution *A*. You will have more of this solution than you need.
2. Make 500 mL of each glucose solution from the stock solution as follows:

   Solution B: 100 mg/dL (1 g/L) = 50 mL of stock + 450 mL of water

   Solution C: 250 mg/dL (2.5 g/L) = 125 mL of stock + 375 mL of water

   Solution D: 500 mg/dL (5 g/L) = 250 mL of stock + 250 mL of water
3. For each group, label 12 tubes as follows: Jorge (0, 0.5, 1.0, 1.5, 2.0, 2.5) and Kyle (0, 0.5, 1.0, 1.5, 2.0, 2.5)
4. Pour 5 mL of the appropriate solution in the following tubes, cap each tube, and place in the racks.

Time (h)	Jorge	Kyle
0	B	C
0.5	C	D
1.0	B	A
1.5	B	A
2.0	B	D
2.5	B	D

5. The solutions should be made the morning of the lab or the day before and stored in a refrigerator overnight. If refrigerated, the solutions should be warmed to room temperature prior to use in the activity.
6. If possible, make color copies of the color scale from the Diastix™ bottle for each group. (Otherwise, a description of the color scale is provided in the activity.)

Teacher Guide and Answers

7. Give each group a copy of the insulin data after they have completed question 6.

Plasma Insulin Concentration (μU/mL)		
Time (h)	**Jorge**	**Kyle**
0	50	25
0.5	80	30
1.0	100	45
1.5	90	50
2.0	60	60
2.5	50	55

Background

When glucose is ingested, it passes through the esophagus and stomach into the small intestine, where it is absorbed into the portal vein. Glucose then passes through the portal vein into the liver prior to entering the general blood circulation. In the liver, glucose is stored as glycogen if insulin is present. The presence of glucose in the small intestine causes the pancreas to release insulin, which allows cells (i.e., liver, muscle, fat) to absorb glucose and causes these cells to store glucose in the form of glycogen and convert glucose to fatty acids. Thus, a spike of insulin precedes a small rise in blood glucose in normal individuals.

The oral glucose tolerance test (OGTT) is a common test for diabetes. To take the OGTT, a person fasts overnight and then drinks a solution containing glucose. Blood glucose levels are checked before drinking the solution and at regular intervals after drinking it. In a person who does not have diabetes (75-g OGTT), the initial reading should be between 60 and 110 mg/dL; after one hour the reading should be less than 200 mg/dL, and after two hours it should be less than 140 mg/dL. Elevated readings might indicate the person has diabetes.

Teaching Tips

Urine glucose tests are not as accurate as blood glucose tests; therefore, blood tests for glucose are greatly preferred. However, the urine might have to be tested for compounds called ketones. The presence of ketones in the urine can help distinguish between type 1 and type 2 diabetes; high levels of ketones can also mean the diabetic should seek the help of a doctor. Therefore, both blood and urine tests have important roles to play in monitoring diabetes.

Answers

1. Kyle's was higher:

   Jorge 100 mg/dL

   Kyle 250 mg/dL
2. Jorge's blood sugar increased from 100 mg/dL to 250 mg/dL within the first half hour and then returned to normal for the rest of the test. In contrast, Kyle's blood glucose started at 250 mg/dL and increased to 500 mg/dL within a half hour. Kyle's blood glucose took longer to decrease and had not returned to pretest levels by the end of the glucose tolerance test.
3. After passing through the mouth, esophagus, and stomach, glucose ends up in the small intestine, where it is absorbed. It passes across the walls of the small intestine into the hepatic portal vein, where it travels to the liver. Once in the liver, glucose is either stored as glycogen or released into the blood stream depending upon whether insulin is present or not. Shortly after a meal, there is a small increase in blood glucose as this process takes place.
4. Yes, for both boys, as mentioned above, glucose increases after a meal. However, because Kyle is diabetic, the changes in his blood glucose levels are exaggerated and the return toward his normal blood glucose level is slowed because he lacks insulin.
5. Jorge's blood glucose is more stable.
6. It appears that Kyle may have diabetes because (1) his pretest or fasting blood glucose level is higher and (2) the changes in his blood glucose levels during the test are exaggerated and uncontrolled.
7. As food (i.e. glucose) enters the small intestine, the pancreas begins to secrete insulin. Therefore, Jorge shows an increase in plasma insulin that peaks at one hour and slowly drops until the end of the test.

Lab 8 ▪ A Sweet Season *continued*

In contrast, Kyle's insulin levels are low and increase slowly throughout the test (but they still remain below normal levels).

8. Plasma insulin in normal individuals increases about the same time that glucose levels begin to rise after the start of the test. They remain elevated throughout most of the test; the elevated insulin levels allow cells to absorb glucose and keep glucose levels near normal while it is absorbed. In the diabetic (Kyle), plasma insulin levels are below normal and rise slowly because Kyle's pancreas does not produce much insulin. This allows Kyle's blood glucose to remain elevated during the test.
9. Kyle has diabetes, probably type 1 because his insulin levels are low. He also exhibits symptoms of diabetes, such as constant hunger and thirst, weight loss, muscle weakness, and inability to withstand fasting between meals.
10. Insulin allows cells to absorb glucose, which lowers blood sugar and keeps it within normal limits after a meal.
11. Jorge will be able to withstand a long period without food because his blood glucose is well controlled. In contrast, Kyle shows wild fluctuations in blood glucose. Because Kyle lacks insulin, his cells cannot absorb and utilize glucose; therefore, his body feels that it is always starved.
12. Kyle does not have sufficient levels of insulin and proper insulin secretion in response to a meal. Therefore, his cells do not absorb and metabolize glucose. His body is in a "starved" state. So, Kyle's body signals him to eat constantly. Furthermore, his body breaks down muscle protein, which is why he feels weak. The elevated blood glucose causes his kidneys to excrete glucose, which also causes more water to be excreted for osmotic reasons. Therefore, Kyle urinates frequently and must drink to avoid dehydration. The elevated blood glucose causes him to feel sleepy, especially after a meal. Despite the increased appetite, Kyle cannot absorb glucose or benefit from the food that he eats; this condition along with the breakdown of muscle protein accounts for the weight loss.
13. Jorge's condition is probably caused by exhaustion from heavy physical activity. He needs rest. In contrast, Kyle has type 1 diabetes (insulin-dependent) and needs insulin treatment as well as proper diet and exercise. His blood glucose should be closely monitored.

Lab 9 ▪ Use Blood Types to Help Solve a Crime

Purpose

The purpose of this lab is to demonstrate a simple blood-typing procedure and the information blood types can provide to forensic investigations.

Biological Concepts

Have students review the following concepts before beginning this activity:

❑ antigen-antibody reactions

❑ blood types

❑ Rhesus blood types

Expected Outcome

Students should be able to determine ABO and Rhesus blood types using antigen-antibody agglutination reactions.

Time

45 minutes

Advance Preparation

- Try to distribute the suspects' blood types roughly according to population parameters. For the U.S. population, these figures are O^+, 38%; O^-, 7%; A^+, 34%; A^-, 6%; B^+, 9%; B^-, 2%; AB^+, 3%; and AB^-, 1%. Assign these sample types to students before class, and record which type each student receives.

Teacher Guide and Answers

Lab 9 ▪ Use Blood Types to Help Solve a Crime *continued*

Teaching Strategies

- Introduce the lab by describing antigen-antibody reactions. Give students an analogy for how antigen-antibody complexes form, such as a lock and key or two jigsaw-puzzle pieces. Explain how the reactions result in the clumping together of red blood cells, which causes the red blood cells to separate out of the fluid portion of blood.
- Point out that blood typing can be quick and easy, as students will see when they do this lab. It can provide quick results before data from more expensive and time-consuming DNA tests are available. However, blood typing cannot conclusively identify an individual, as DNA analysis can.
- Be sure the investigation is carried out in a well-ventilated room. Fumes may be hazardous to students with breathing difficulties such as asthma.

Teaching Tips

- All used blood-typing cards and other materials possibly contaminated with blood should be promptly disposed of as biological hazardous waste. Follow proper precautions.

Answers

1. Students should rule out all suspects who do not have A^+ blood.
2. Too many people share the same blood type for blood type alone to prove conclusively who committed a crime.
3. The more blood groups you added, the more you could narrow down the list of potential perpetrators, at least to the extent that the additional blood types varied among suspects.
4. A less variable blood-group system would generally be less useful for forensic analysis because most people would have the same blood type.

Lab 10 ▪ The Missing Restaurant Owner

Purpose

This activity is about the uses of forensic science in a murder case. The students play the role of forensic scientist and use blood typing data, genetic analysis, and DNA typing to identify the victim in the absence of a body or murder weapon. The activity fits well after discussions of genetics, blood grouping, and DNA technology.

Biological Concepts

Have students review the following concepts before beginning this activity:

❑ blood type analysis

❑ DNA analysis

Time

30–45 minutes

Teaching Strategies

- This activity can be done by individuals, in groups, or as a class discussion. Because the story builds section by section, it would be best to give the students one section at a time.
- The activity lends itself to debates on justice and the presence of physical evidence, and students must synthesize conclusions and opinions from several lines of evidence.

Answers

1. Blood Types:

Father	A
Mother	B
Suspect	O
Clothing	O
Restaurant office	O
Watch	O

Teacher Guide and Answers

Lab 10 ▪ The Missing Restaurant Owner

continued

2. Yes, it is possible that the blood found in the restaurant office and on the clothing belonged to the missing restaurant owner, even though the father was type A and the mother was type B. If both parents were heterozygotes, then their offspring would have the following possible blood types: A, B, AB, and O.
3. Yes. The blood on the watch, in the office, and on the clothing shares genetic elements (bands) with both the mother (A) and the father (B), but not with the suspect (C). This indicates that the blood on the evidence was not that of the suspect. Because it shares elements with the father and mother, the blood must have come from someone closely related to them.
4. The answer to this question is open to debate by students. The probability that the blood samples belong to the missing restaurant owner place him in the office where the crime allegedly took place. The blood samples and the strands of the victim's hair place him in the trunk of the suspect's car and in the countryside. The data would indicate that the suspect murdered the restaurant owner in the office, placed his body in the trunk of his car, and disposed of the body somewhere in the countryside. However, one might argue that you need a body and a weapon to conclusively prove that there was indeed a murder.
5. Answers will vary based on students' opinions and interpretations of the evidence as described in question 4. One could argue that murder convictions require a body, a weapon, opportunity, and motive. Although the suspect had motive and opportunity, there is no body or murder weapon to conclusively prove that the missing owner was actually murdered.